*THE DEFINITIVE STUDY OF
THE ACCURACY OF THE WORLD'S
FOREMOST PSYCHIC*

For forty-three years, in over 15,000 Life
Readings, Edgar Cayce astonished and amazed
the world with his controversial prophecies, predictions and teachings. In this definitive study of
the accuracy of the world's foremost psychic,
Lytle Robinson uses historical records, interviews,
court documents and the latest scientific breakthroughs to evaluate and analyze Cayce's teachings and claims. It is a book that will surprise
some, awe and amaze many, and fascinate everyone!

*"Cayce made some apparent, horrendous mistakes. Yet
many of his claims concur with the latest thinking . . .
Cayce was* avant-garde *(ahead of his time) and that is
always perilous . . ."*

—LYTLE W. ROBINSON

IS IT TRUE WHAT THEY SAY ABOUT Edgar Cayce?

LYTLE W. ROBINSON

BERKLEY BOOKS, NEW YORK

For Barbara, Carolyn, Stephen, David, and Tanya

This Berkley book contains the complete
text of the original hardcover edition.
It has been completely reset in a type face
designed for easy reading, and was printed
from new film.

IS IT TRUE WHAT
THEY SAY ABOUT
EDGAR CAYCE?

A Berkley Book / published by arrangement with
Vulcan Books

PRINTING HISTORY
First published in Great Britain in 1979 by
Neville Spearman (Jersey) Limited
Vulcan Books edition published 1979
Berkley edition / January 1981

ISBN: 0-425-04735-0

A BERKLEY BOOK ® TM 757,375
Berkley Books are published by Berkley Publishing Corporation,
200 Madison Avenue, New York, New York 10016.
PRINTED IN THE UNITED STATES OF AMERICA

CONTENTS

PREFACE

Since his death in 1945, Edgar Cayce has become the world's most famous psychic; more has been written about him and his "readings" than any other modern clairvoyant. Much of it, however, presents only the favorable, although the Virginia Beach seer made no claim of infallibility.

In this sequel to *Edgar Cayce's Story of the Origin and Destiny of Man*, I have attempted to search out the truth or untruth of some of the statements he made over a period of forty-two years. How often was the sleeping psychic correct, or incorrect? That is the paramount question I have endeavored to answer. Correlating information from the unconscious world by conscious means and methods, however, has its limitations. Science itself is not infallible.

Needless to say, the opinions, interpretations, and conclusions are mine, and they are indeed fallible. They are not necessarily the views of the Association for Research and Enlightenment or the Edgar Cayce Foundation.

I should add that I had no idea in the beginning how this study would conclude. I was as curious as any reader.

L.W.R.

Tucson, Arizona
September, 1978

ix

INTRODUCTION

An impending sense of change is pervading the world of socio–economic–religious ideas. The reigning wisdom of past decades is under cross-examination; rationalism, scientism, materialism are being challenged. At the center of the ferment is the belated realization that man and his mores are more complex than the experts thought. Conventional solutions are proving less certain than advertised, for the whole man has been sacrificed for concentration on his parts. Man is not a machine. And he is more than a rat in a laboratory or a chimpanzee in a cage.

The mind and personality, for example, have been reduced to nothing more than machinations of the brain, although man doesn't own the largest brain. The human engineering of the Behaviorists is headed for certain bankruptcy, if for no other reason than man's determined, persistent spiritual quest, dating back to the most primitive cultures. To the Behaviorists such as B. F. Skinner, observable behavior is the only reality, and belief in an inner man is mere superstition. "Something going on inside the individual, states of mind, feelings, purposes, expectancies", are fictions, says Skinner. Man is wholly and solely conditioned by his environment. He is a will-less piece of machinery that can be turned into a robot. But Skinnerites tread firmer ground when they assert that an improved man will emerge from an improved society.

Freud, on the other hand, believed in the inner man, but placed religion in "the category of the neurosis of mankind". Yet in his latter days, he wrote Hereward Carrington that if he were starting over he would devote his life to psychical research; he came to accept thought transference among other phenomena. But Carl Jung, the Swiss psychologist, was the first to recognize man's psychical complex and the collective unconscious.

Today, the new thought tends more toward Jung than to Freud. Psychotherapist Rollo May, in his volume, *Power and Innocence*, writes, "My faith is that the human being will be rediscovered", and with it come new emphasis on love, creativity, music and other qualitative, introspective experiences. Man has an immense capacity for individualism: integrity, responsibility, compassion, rebellion, hate, jealousy, idiosyncrasy. He cannot be molded and conditioned *en masse*. There will always be the renegades, the mavericks, the non-conformists.

One of the most outspoken men of anti-science is Theodore Roszak, the Berkeley, California, historian. Science's alleged objectivity along with its attendant evils, he believes, have denatured man's personal experiences and taken the mystery and sacredness out of life. Reason is a limited skill, and it is only one of man's many capabilities, overlooking his "spiritual knowledge and power". "Here is a range of experience that we are screening out of our experience in the name of knowledge," he says.

We have come to think of knowledge as explicit, rational, logical, but just as important are mystery, ambiguity, illogic, contradiction, and transcendent experience. The difficulty is that they are not easy to explain and are therefore relegated to the ashcan of the "mystical" and the "occult".

Geologist Frank Rhodes, dean of Liberal Arts at the University of Michigan, puts it bluntly: "It may be that the qualities we measure have as little relation to the world itself as a telephone number to its subscriber."

And, declares Richard Bube, professor of Materials Science and Electrical Engineering at Stanford, "One of the most pernicious falsehoods ever to be almost universally accepted is that the scientific method is the only reliable way to truth." Science's observations are not altogether "theory-neutral", says Harvard's Everett Mendelsohn, as it once claimed, but are actually "theory-laden". There sometimes is as much search as research to prove a thesis, as every writer, lawyer, and debater knows.

From the scientific point of view, we may never learn how the universe began or what are its ultimate building blocks. Physics has already discovered more than fifteen subatomic particles, and we still don't know why or what makes them tick. The solar system, it finally begins to appear, is a ball of energy and matter is an illusion. The only reality, in the final analysis, may be some kind of electro-spiritual vibration.

The eminent German physicist–philosopher, Carl Friedrich von Weizacker, believes that some aspects of mysticism will be incorporated within the scientific framework. His institute near Munich is attempting to show the essential convergence between Eastern mysticism and Western science. He is convinced that "mysticism is one of the great discoveries of mankind", and that "It may turn out to be far more important than our time is inclined to believe." If the professor retains his head and his hide, he may indeed cut a swath through the jungle of the unknown.

Few American scientists, however, would agree, and fewer still are ready to discard the old mechanistic rationality. At best, they are merely tolerant of their critics' suggestion that science does not have the Whole Truth and Nothing but the Truth. Nevertheless, new paths are being tread through old frontiers—the mysteries of the human mind and personality.

Parapsychology is slowly becoming recognized as a legitimate field of inquiry. As always, for the pioneers cutting a new trail, the way has not been easy. One of the biggest thorns was Dr. George R. Price, who in

1955, published an article in the prestigious journal, *Science*, accusing J. B. Rhine and S. G. Soal of fraud in their work on extrasensory perception. But in the January 28, 1972 issue, Price confesses to a change of heart and mind. "During the past year, I have had some correspondence with J. B. Rhine which has convinced me that I was highly unfair to him in what I said . . . The article discussed possible fraud in extrasensory perception experiments. I suspect that I was similarly unfair in what I said about S. G. Soal in that paper."

Few scientific claims today are fraudulent, but many are of dubious merit, especially as to conclusion. The facts may be correct and the interpretation in total error. Rapid eye movements (REM), for instance, mean that the sleeper is watching his dreams, but fetuses also exhibit REM, which gives birth to another set of problems. Defeated wolves humbly offer their throats to their opponents, it is claimed, who nobly refrain from biting a brother while he is down; instead, the victors urinate to celebrate their triumph. The first wolf is just as likely exhausted and surrenders, while the victor goes off to urinate because of the exercise or because he wanted to all along. Man is superior thanks to an opposable thumb, but there is a frog with an opposable thumb and it hasn't become a superfrog. And bears mark trees by rubbing fur on them as a sign to other bears, not simply because they itch!

But men of science are not altogether to blame for this state of affairs. The popular press in its propensity for the dramatic and the sensational, encourages overdrawn reporting and therefore must share responsibility for many conventional misconceptions. In the hands of pseudo-scientific writers, theory is elevated to fact, hypothesis turned into dogma. The reader is sold a bill of questionable goods if not phoney baloney.

We need to re-examine some of our well-worn intellectual ruts and seek other fertile fields of inquiry. Modern science is not infallible, although it's still the best information we have. What it teaches today is different from what it believed fifty years ago, and we can be sure it will be vastly different fifty years hence. Our technology has established many facts beyond a reasonable doublt, but science has many theories and postulations based on assumption, conjecture, and the rankest kind of speculation, as we shall see. Far-reaching theories are spun from flimsy evidence that appall the discriminating layman who presumes the case to be reasonably air-tight. Science may be the modern messiah to some, but it too has its illusions. No person is easier to fool than one's self. Our capacity for self-deception is nearly infinite; we are apt to believe what we want to believe.

This is true of the professional as well as the layman. Nothing is quite so repelling to man as the thought of a new idea—especially another's idea. If it contradicts one's own beliefs, it is, *ipso facto*, absurd, impossible, imaginary. The truth is that we do not have as much truth as we think we do. And a good part of what we "know" is superficial. In our simplicity, we have become so smart that we sometimes outsmart ourselves. The cynic, for instance, may in reality be a frustrated idealist.

"It has been proved to be a myth," writes Sally Bates, associate editor of science for *Saturday Review*, "that anthropology, the 'science of man', is a discipline with concepts and theories based on objective work by professional scholars. As many anthropologists now realize, claims of scientific 'objectivity' are apt to be inflated and scholarly activities are not without political overtones . . ."

Robert Ornstein, in his book, *The Psychology of Consciousness*, emphasizes the importance for scientists to recognize that their methods provide knowledge of only one type of reality, and that there exists "a separate reality" which must be apprehended intuitively, through legitimate, but non-ordinary modes of consciousness. Science will achieve its first understanding of intuitive, mystical philosophies by interpreting experiences in their own terms. REM, for instance, gave the Behaviorists their first entree to the objective study of dreams, which were wrested from the realm of scientific prejudice only a few decades ago, primarily by Freud, Adler, and Jung.

The story is told—apocryphal no doubt—of the scientist who trained a flea to jump at the sound of a bell. After each jump, he would pull off a leg of the insect. When the poor creature had only one leg left, he rang the bell and the flea flopped over weakly. Then the scientist removed the last leg and rang the bell. Nothing happened. His conclusion: When you remove all the legs of flea, it goes deaf.

A public opinion poll of "realistic, materialistic" Americans revealed that 74 percent still believe in survival after death. And this was not necessarily the result of religious training or conviction. Contrary to our modern, pragmatic, scientific attitudes, most Americans apparently look to the "super natural" in search of their true identity. Ninety-four percent believe in God. Hypotheses, postulations, and theories simply do not render satisfying, enduring answers to the complexities of human existence in the earth and the need for spiritual sustenance.

That man does not live by bread alone is evidenced by orthodox religions, the emotional Pentecostal movement among the inarticulate and the unsophisticated; and the phenomenal growth of interest in the psychic and the occult. The study of dreams, meditation, yoga, astrology, mysticism, ESP demonstrates a need, a searching for a more profound meaning and purpose in life. The vacuum left by a materialistic science and an over-simplified conventional religion is being filled. Institutional religions are on the decline because they offer so few answers to an inquisitive, educated generation.

The New York Times Book Review has estimated that publication of hardback books in the field of the supernatural is four times what it was ten years ago. In paperbacks, over 200 titles on parapsychology and related subjects were listed at one time. Even the big popular magazines have entered the once frowned upon arena.

And Ruth Montgomery, author of volumes on reincarnation, accepted an invitation to speak on "The Psychic" at Notre Dame. Hugh Lynn Cayce, Director of the Edgar Cayce Foundation at Virginia Beach, Virginia, has lectured on campuses and in churches, once considered hostile territory. One hundred colleges now offer courses in parapsychology.

Predictably, the enormous interest has spawned a spate of kooks, krooks, and krackpots. Charlatan "gurus", "psychics", "sensitives", and "mediums" prey on the naive and the gullible. The psychic became the study of the id by the odd. Most of what they say cannot be documented. It is all too easy to preach sermons or spin beautiful yarns of past incarnations in some remote and romantic historical period that cannot be checked.

Although ESP has been fairly well established except for the most hard-nosed, other psychic phenomena are even more difficult to prove beyond a shadow of a doubt. Subjects tend to tighten up under laboratory conditions and their ability, far from consistent, varies from time to time according to mood and environment.

But America did have one psychic who is well documented and can be checked. What he had to say while in a state of deep sleep is still on file at Virginia Beach. There is little question that Edgar Cayce was clairvoyant; the real question is, how accurate are his "readings"? Was he infallible? If not, when, where, how, and why did he fail? How many of his statements can be verified? How many refuted? In brief, just how accurate was Edgar Cayce?

That is the purpose of this study. And we will endeavor to turn a cold, objective, skeptical eye on his readings, comparing them with the latest knowledge available.

Fortunately, Cayce gave perhaps 15,000 odd readings—some very odd—between 1901 and 1944. Unfortunately, not all are extant, but most are and some of the statements he made are checkable. Rapidly becoming the world's most quoted psychic, his work is better known today than when he was alive. More has been written and said about him than any other modern clairvoyant, and numerous volumes have been translated into French, German, Portuguese, Spanish, Japanese, Sinhalese. His principal biography, *There Is A River*, by Thomas Sugrue, first published in 1943, is now in its 18th printing. Yet the volume for many years sold only 10,000 copies. Later, the paperback edition reached a half-million copies and both are still selling.

The story of how it first came to be published is as strange as Cayce's discourses. William Sloane, then an editor at Henry Holt & Co., heard of the work and its difficulty in finding a home. "I asked to see the manuscript," he recalled many years later, "but the material was so extraordinary I felt I ought to check on Cayce's ability."

A child of his had been complaining of a painful jaw. Sloane saw the possibilities and decided to get a reading from Cayce. When the report came back, it claimed there was an infection behind a certain tooth. It ought to be extracted. Sloane took the child to the dentist, but he rejected the idea, saying there was nothing wrong with the tooth. Sloane insisted, and had to finally demand that the tooth be pulled. "So the dentist pulled the tooth," he recalled. "The infection was there. The pain went away. And I published Tom Sugrue's book under the title of *There Is A River*."

In 1956, Morey Bernstein, inspired by the Cayce records, wrote *The Search For Bridey Murphy*. It sold 150,000 copies in six weeks before being smeared by a fundamentalist preacher and the Chicago *American*. Most of their criticisms and that of others have since been refuted and new ground was plowed in the field of the psychic. Reincarnation, once discussed only in whispers, became fashionable.

In 1967, Jess Stern's story of Cayce, *The Sleeping Prophet*, was published. It hit the best seller lists for more than six months and the presses turned out 250,000 copies plus over a million more in paperback. Cayce's name became a household word. Altogether, some seven million copies under three dozen different titles on his life and works have been printed in this country and abroad. A 90-minute CBS-tv special has been shown, entitled "Atlantis, Bimini, and Edgar Cayce".

In hundreds of cases the readings have demonstrated themselves to be honest and accurate. Many have been well publicized and we will for the most part, not repeat them here. Our chief interest is in the predictions, claims, side remarks, and passing comments that Cayce made which have been neither verified nor refuted. One could spend a lifetime attempting to check out everything Cayce said and still not complete the task. Fourteen million words from an unconscious mind on an enormous range of subject matter, some in specialized fields such as medicine, await more competent researchers. We will confine ourselves to some of the most interesting and important problems Cayce raised that can be checked, remembering in certain instances that the readings were usually for specific individuals and what may be true for one person would not necessarily be true for all.

How accurate was Edgar Cayce? We will endeavor to ferret out the truth or untruth of many of his assertions that appear to have questionable substantive support. The corroborating or contravening evidence presented —from reliable, authoritative, non-psychic sources—is not always conclusive, but merely evidential. Proof beyond the shadow of a doubt is almost impossible. In the final analysis, one can only weigh and evaluate from one's own experiences. The ring of truth has a different sound for each of us. We must judge for ourselves.

In this study, a sequel to *Edgar Cayce's Story of the Origin and Destiny of Man*, published in 1972, we have the opportunity to explore in more depth some of the claims made by the world's most talked about psychic.

On People, Places and Things

He was not a very impressive youth—spoiled, self-centered, of narrow interests. Yet his life reading given at the time of birth said in his last incarnation he was Thomas Jefferson. He in no way resembled that great statesman of American history whose profound philosophy of freedom, equality, and democratic principles has affected peoples and constitutions around the world.

"If there is anything that makes me doubt the readings," said one dedicated, long-time, Cayce staff lecturer who knew him well, "it is that that boy could have been Thomas Jefferson!" Today he loves the beaches and does odd jobs.

There is, of course, almost no way to prove or disprove such a claim, especially of famous people.

Next to predictions, the Edgar Cayce readings appear most vulnerable in the specifics of purported past incarnations, an area of research that on the surface might seem relatively easy for recent periods of history. But, alas, tracking down the names of people mentioned in Life Readings is like plowing a mud hole in a swamp. Some personalities, such as "James Johnson", who supposedly came to "the western shores" of this country seeking the "treasure of the earth's storehouse" in the "vicinity of what is now Eldora Pass, California", are impossible to confirm. (*Case #4713-1*)

For one thing, the name is much too common. The telephone directory of Tucson, Arizona, for example, lists twelve "James Johnsons", plus many more with initials only. The time factor, for another, is uncertain—although presumably it was during the gold rush days. Other difficulties are the absence of official records, the non-ownership of any property, the obscurity of the individual. While there may be indeed have been any number of James Johnson's, there is no "Eldora Pass" in California!

Just as frustrating is the incompleteness of official records and the late date they were instituted in certain regions. An example of this is the case of "Ida Hemmingway". Cayce said she was a Virginian who came with her husband—not too happily—to Arizona in 1842. They settled "nine miles northwest of Tucson", and she died within the year. Here we have specifics, but Pima County records were initiated at a later date, 1861. Moreover, there are no graveyards of the period; the deceased were buried in the desert.

Conversely, the mention of famous personalities—which was rare—is worthless and proves nothing unless some generally unknown sidelight of that sojourn is revealed and confirmed; such persons are too well known and Cayce was saying nothing new. But occasionally a name crops up that is useful and can be checked. This same "James Johnson", in a previous incarnation, was also one "Earl Warwick" in England, Cayce said.

"In the one before this we find in the English rule of George the First in England. Then in the name of Earl Warwick and in the House of Commons. History will be found of this individual, as we will see. In the urges then as will be in the present entity: That of the domineering spirit of self's development pertaining to knowledge. Hence the training that will be necessary in earthly development in the earth's plane of unselfishness." (*Case #4713-1*)

No history of Earl Warwick can be found, but if Cayce meant the Earl of Warwick, as well he may, what

he had to say is substantially correct although little of
his character can be determined.

Earl of Warwick is an English title bestowed on different persons of different families dating sporadically
back to the year 1088. The title lapsed from time to
time, but in 1706 during the rule of King George I,
Robert Rich succeeded to the title and the estate and
became Earl of Warwick. He served four terms in the
House of Commons, not consecutively, from 1715 to
1741, from three different districts. A military officer,
he fought against the French, and once dueled Sir Ed-
mund Bacon, seriously wounding him. As Sir Robert
Rich, he attained the rank of Lt. General and Marshal,
dying in 1768 at the age of 82.

Unfortunately, we learn little of his personality from
our reference source, *The Dictionary of National
Biography*. First printed in 1917, it was republished in
several volumes in 1921-22 by Oxford University Press.
It is improbable that Cayce, living in a small community, had access to this information.

One diligent researcher, who prefers to remain
anonymous, has brought interesting but not altogether
conclusive results in tracing names of people Cayce
mentions. In one case, an incarnation was given for a
"John Dain", supposedly living during the pioneer days
of early New England. "The entity among those who
first landed in that country now known as Massachusetts, and among those called the Puritans. Then in the
name of John Dain, and the entity gained in that period,
through the service rendered to others, and through the
application of self to the building in body, in mind, in
the structures for the body and for the mind, as the entity endured during that period much suffering." (*Case
#571-2*)

The first Puritans arrived on the *Mayflower* in 1620,
and others followed soon thereafter. By 1640 there were
eight villages and a population of 2500 people. The infamous persecution trials occurred during the years after 1688, and the Plymouth Colony also suffered

severely from the Indian attacks of the 17th and early 18th centuries.

Our researcher uncovered two volumes carrying references to a "John Dane", and the reader will note the difference in spelling. Considering the semi-literacy of the time, misspellings and poor handwriting, the evolution in the spelling of proper names is not uncommon. A volume entitled *Witchcraft*, by Charles Williams, published by Faber & Faber, London, gives an account of how a group "signed a statement wherein forgiveness was asked for having had a hand in the persecutions". Among them was John Dane.

The reading doesn't mention this important facet of his life, saying, "The urge as is seen from this . . . that of the natural builder, especially in those of mechanical natures . . . the love for those conditions that apply to nature, in its ability to give to man material benefits in that of those that act as aids to man's influence." We learn little from that, but it's possible that Dane, the good Puritan and lover of nature, indulged in witch hunting in his youth and later lived to regret it. But we cannot be certain of this, or if he is the right "John Dain", or even if there was such a John Dain.

In another early reading, Cayce relates a story of one "Allen", a minister in Salem during the persecutions. "Before this we find the entity in the land of the present nativity, during those periods when there were those sojournings of many peoples in this present land, and when there were the questionings as to the experiences that were being had by many in the entity's parish; for he—or the entity, Allen then—was a minister in that land now known as Salem—or the Providence Town lands, for this, as is seen, is a parish that was covered then by Allen . . . and there may be found as yet the monuments or the little slab here, as we find, in the outer portion of Salem, in what is called Massachusetts, of Allen, the minister to this church." (*Case #509-1*)

Here at last is something tangible with which to work, for we learn of his employment, environment, character, and definite location. "The entity in the experience suffered through the persecutions that were brought on the physical body", for his apparent attempts to "clarify the conditions for the peoples and for those that were . . . persecuted". This "brought such turmoil" to him. "Yet the entity within itself gained throughout the experience. Though banished, yet loved by all those whom the entity served in body and in mind during that sojourn."

The name of Reverend James Allen turns up in *Records of Salem Witchcraft*, Vol. II, by W. Elliot Woodward, where he is quoted as saying, "I have lived nine years at Salisbury in the work of the ministry and now four years in the office of Pastour."

But his reputed grave marker, after much searching, has never been found. Many are toppled over face down and not easy to lift. Some no doubt are buried under eroded soil. Others simply have vanished, for they made good walkways, hearth stones, drainage boards. After all, who cared about an old abandoned cemetery!

The case of a man named "Jamerson", who supposedly lived in the Revolutionary War period, is likewise evidential but not conclusive. "Before this the entity was in that experience when there were many changes being made in the relationships of the peoples of the land of the present nativity, during those sojourns when there were the wars and the activities of same in those periods known as 1776 to 1800.

"The entity sojourned in that land near to where the activities were begun in the present experience, in the name Jamerson. In that experience the entity found much that brought turmoil through the physical activities of those about self, yet made for those sojourns that have set determinations and ideals and purposes as those factors in the experiences of all that will bring the fruits of that sown in the mental and spiritual self in its activities day by day." (*Case #540–1*)

Unhappily again, no first name was given, but research revealed a reference in a book by W.T.R. Saffell, published in 1894 under the title, *Records of the*

Revolutionary War. It lists ''The Sixth Captain's Company . . . privates for three years (including) Thomas Jamerson, enlisted February 22, 1778.''

Cayce's frequent omission of first names is frustrating, and one can only wish he had given more specific historical references that could be validated. Yet in all fairness, the Life Readings were not intended to be historical treatises but summaries of spiritual development that would be meaningful and useful to the recipient today. They are filled with preachments and lacking in flattery.

Yet Cayce himself sometimes gave advice on where records could be found. A notable example is that of Barnett Seay, a Confederate soldier who had lived in Henrico County, Virginia, where the inquirer was told his identity could be established. The man later made a trip to Richmond but could find no record. A Clerk of Court, however, told him that many of the early registries had recently been moved to the Department of Old Records of the Virginia State Historical Library. There, after some searching of archives, he finally located ''himself''. Barnett A. Seay had enlisted in Lee's army as a colorbearer in 1862, at the age of 21.

The Dead and the Missing

Cayce's discourses are notably poor when the request came from other than the inquirer himself or from those very close to him. He once gave a reading for a child who had unknowingly died of leukemia the day before. The request had come from a woman vaguely interested in the publicized case but who was not related to the child. The conductor held a newspaper clipping in her hand as Cayce went to sleep. ''Yes, we find the experimentations that are being made with this body are at the present somewhat more helpful than has been and is ordinarily found in conditions of this nature and character, in one of such stages. Should there continue to be the decrease in the red blood count—don't make so much disturbance, but—we would suggest that there be first a minute injection to the body of the properties that tend to make for the drying of lymph. Atropine, see? First make this injection—one eightieth of a grain, hypodermically. Preferably make this in the area near the spleen."

He went on to prescribe a blood transfusion, atomidine, beef juice, iron. "And we should save these conditions," he said. In closing he commented, "Should there be the response, we find that these applications would be the most effective for those with leukemia, in such stages of development—or ages." (*Case #534-1*)

The reading seems to be more on the disease than on the child, who was already dead. Yet on three other occasions Cayce indicated the body was dying, and he proved to be correct.

In one famous case his information was equally useless under circumstances where he should have proved his clairvoyance beyond any doubt. A series of readings was taken on Amelia Earhart, the aviatrix lost in July, 1937. One request came from her husband through friends. Cayce declared she and her co-pilot, Fred Noolan, had run out of gasoline and that they were alive and in fair condition at a location 90 miles northwest of Howland Island in the Pacific. This was far, far off course, and, moreover, there is no land 90 mile northwest of Howland Island.

The following month, August, he gave another reading saying she had died of heat and exposure. Yet neither Amelia Earhart, Fred Noolan, or the plane have ever been found. One practical version today is that they were on a spy mission and were captured by the Japanese and beheaded. If true, their publicized flight course was part of the "cover story".

Another version, hinted at but not established by the release of FBI files in 1973, is that she may not have been captured and executed as a spy, and, implausibly, could still be alive at the age of seventy-five. The "evidence" consists of the following:

An American GI stationed in the Philippines before Pearl Harbor overheard a conversation between two

Japanese—"Amelia Earhart is still alive and is being detained in a hotel in Tokyo." Later, after the Japanese took the islands, one of their intelligence officers told him, "Don't worry about her well-being. She is perfectly all right." Other items in the file relate reports that Noonan was thought to be alive ten years after the disappearance and speculate that his "recovery within a nominal time appears quite fairly probable". Some Japanese said they had "heard her over the radio", others that they had heard she was "alive and in Tokyo".

The trouble with all this is that the FBI is known to put almost anything in a person's file—rumor, gossip, hearsay, neighborhood quarrels; peace-marchers, anti-establishmentarians. The material is often raw, unevaluated and unsubstantiated. Millions of American citizens are unknowingly dossiered in FBI, CIA and Army Intelligence files with spurious information.

The Lindbergh Kidnapping

In the most notorious criminal case of his time, Cayce again had the opportunity to prove his psychic abilities to a skeptical world. On March 1, 1932, twenty-one-month-old Charles A. Lindbergh, Jr., mysteriously disappeared from his crib in Hopewell, N.J. On the sill of his second-story window was a ransom note demanding $50,000. Outside was a ladder. Thus began America's most bizarre and publicized kidnapping case.

On March 9, Cayce gave a reading requested by a friend of the Lindbergh's. The dissertation indicated three men and a woman had the child in a house in the mill section of New Haven, called Cardova, on a street named Schartest. The house was described as a two-story shingle painted brown. The child's hair had been cut and dyed.

Attempts to locate such an area and house failed, for he gave no specific address. Evidently disappointed himself, Cayce wrote a friend and intermediary, "I have always had my doubts about anything very authentic on such matters unless it came of itself through individuals deeply involved." Subsequent readings were as confusing and unrevealing. Jersey City was mentioned, and vaguely described streets and neighborhoods which no one could find.

Within a few days, a second, then a third ransom note were passed to the Lindberghs. On April 2, $50,000 in marked bills was handed over in a Bronx cemetery, but the infant was not returned. Then on May 12, the partially decomposed body of Charles, Jr., was uncovered on the Lindbergh estate. Death had occurred, an autopsy disclosed, on the night of the kidnapping.

For more than two years the nation-wide manhunt continued without result. Then in September, 1934, an alert garage attendant was handed a $10 gold certificate in payment for gasoline. Suspicious, he noted the license number and notified authorities. The trail led to Bruno Richard Hauptmann, an unemployed carpenter. Found in his Bronx home were $13,750 of the ransom money and the telephone number of the go-between, Dr. John F. Condon. One of the rungs of the ladder, it was ascertained, had come from flooring in the Hauptmann house, and his handwriting matched that in the notes.

In December, 1935, Cayce suggested that Hauptmann was only partly guilty. The case went to trial in January, and forty-five days later Hauptmann was found guilty on strong circumstantial evidence. The possibility of others being involved never entered the case, and Hauptmann defiantly denied his guilt throughout. On April 3, 1936, he was executed in the electric chair, invoking the name of the Lord as witness to his innocence. For a supposedly religious man about to face his maker, this is unsettling. We'll never know the whole truth about the Lindbergh case.

In a recent book, *Scapegoat: The Lonesome Death of Bruno Richard Hauptmann*, Anthony Scaduto maintains that the evidence was framed by the police, that Hauptmann worked that day, and that no motive was established. Moreover, Governor Hoffman offered a possible commutation of sentence if he would confess, and Hauptmann refused. Why the offer?

If he was only "partly guilty", as Cayce claimed—presumably meaning one of a conspiracy—he may not have committed the actual crime. If true, the question arises, who was he protecting?

Cayce once made an insignificant passing remark: "Winterthur, Switzerland—what a pretty stream! Good fishing there!"

The train from Geneva to Lake Constance passes through Winterthur, and there is indeed a picturesque stream *en route*, just outside of the town. "Any fish in there?" a local native was asked.

"Ah, yes," he answered. "Plenty fish."

Where is John Peniel?

In 1934 before a small group of followers, Cayce was queried "regarding the spiritual, mental and physical changes which are coming to the earth". In the course of this dissertation he made one of his most melocramatic claims.

"There is soon to come into the world a body; one of our own number here that to many has been a representative of a sect, of a thought, of a philosophy, of a group, yet one beloved of all men in all places where the universality of God in the earth has been proclaimed, where the oneness of the Father as God is known and is consciously magnified in the activities of individuals that proclaim the acceptable day of the Lord. Hence that one John, the beloved in the earth—his name shall be John, and also at the place where he met face to face (*sic*). He comes as a messenger, not as a forerunner but as a messenger; for these are periods when mental, material, are to be so altered in the affairs of men as to be even bringing turmoil to those that have not seen that the Spirit is moving in His ways to bring the knowledge of the Father in the hearts and lives of men.

"When, where, is to be this one? In the hearts and minds of those that have set themselves in that position that they become a channel through which spiritual, mental and material things become one in the purpose and desires of that physical body!

"As to the material changes that are to be as an omen, as a sign to those that this is shortly to come to pass—as has been given of old, the sun will be darkened and the earth shall be broken up in divers places—and *then* shall be *proclaimed*—through the spiritual interception in the hearts and minds and souls of those that have sought His way—that *His* star has appeared, and will point the way for those that enter into the holy of holies in themselves. For, God the Father, God the teacher, God the director, in the minds and hearts of men, must ever be *in* those that come to know Him as first and foremost in the seeking of those souls; for He is first the *God* to the individual and as He is exemplified, as He is manifested in the heart and in the acts of the body of the individual, He becomes manifested before men. And those that seek in the latter portion of the year of Lord as ye have counted in and among men, '36, he will appear!"

In the next two paragraphs Cayce enumerates certain land changes and political upheavals that will be discussed in later chapters. Then he says: "Who shall proclaim the acceptable year of the Lord in him that has been born in the earth in America? Those from that land where there has been the regeneration, not only of the body but the mind and the spirit of man, *they* shall come and declare that John Peniel is giving to the world the new order of things. Not that these that have been proclaimed have been refused, but that they are made *plain* in the minds of men, that they may know the truth; and the truth, the life, the light will make them free."

"John", if born in 1936, would now be 43 years old, and as a great spiritual leader, it is getting rather late for him to be "proclaimed", or even be self-proclaimed. Not even a faker has come forth as Pretender to the Throne of Fame, nor have the dire signs and omens come about.

It all could happen yet, some may say, and John has simply chosen at this point in events to not let himself be known as The Messenger. The trouble with this bit of rationalization is that we don't even have a great religious leader named John Peniel. Moreover, he is to usher in the New Order, which suggests that he might be something of a political figure as well. And again we draw a blank.

Yet Cayce was uncannily accurate in many of his other predictions. In 1939, he said there would be serious racial strife in the United States just before and after the death of the "second President" who would die in Office—John F. Kennedy. In April 1929 he forecast an imminent Wall Street crash. It came in October. In 1931 he predicted better things for America—"in the spring of '33 will be the real definite improvements". Franklin Roosevelt and his New Deal for the common man came into power in March of that year. In August of 1941 he told a young man entering the military service not to expect to get out until 1945, when the war would end. During the Depression he advised friends to buy property on the north side of Virginia Beach, not to the south which was being heavily promoted. The south side never developed and the city's growth has long been to the north.

The perplexing question about Cayce is how can he be so right and still be so wrong? Moreover, he can be wrong today and right tomorrow, and vice versa.

Silver, Gold and Oil

Cayce didn't do much better in seeking out the treasures of the earth. He was wrong on buried pirated gold, Indian artifacts, the famous "Lost Dutchman Mine" in Arizona, oil fields in Texas—although at least one turned out to be a gusher.

In the 1920's, he was seeking money to build a hospital. A friend, David Kahn, suggested a reading on the location of oil. Oddly, the reading said that if they would go to Luling, Texas, they would meet a man on the courthouse steps who would tell them where to find it in the county. Kahn later related the story as follows: "When we got to the courthouse, I saw an elderly man coming down the steps carrying a cane. I went up to him and I said, 'Pardon me, sir, my name is David E. Kahn, and I am here investigating any possible oil formation in this area.'

"His answer was, 'Well, you couldn't have picked a better man.' He explained that he was a county judge. He had lived in the area many years and knew its formations intimately . . . and suggested a site some miles out of town."

The tract turned out to be an area of poor, black, dirt farmers whose cattle sometimes refused to drink the water. Cayce went to sleep on the ground and said, according to Kahn, "If you will drill under the tree you will get oil within three hundred feet but you will also get oil throughout the area. It is a great salt dome loaded with the richest oil in Texas."

Kahn immediately advanced a few hundred dollars for a five-year lease on three thousand acres of land; the owners were to get the customary one-seventh of any profits, Kahn, Cayce and their backers the rest, all at their expense.

Then the troubles started. There were problems with drillers and their employees, antagonisms, competition, sabotage of equipment. It became costly, and the little group soon ran out of funds, before striking any oil. They had to give up their lease and abandon the project.

But a year and a half later Kahn received a newspaper clipping from an acquaintance. The headline read: LULING TEXAS AFLOW. The property was the same Cayce had gone to sleep on. Eventually, fourteen wells were dug, and they all came in. The property sold for twelve million dollars.

Cayce once gave many dissertations to seekers after a buried "pirate treasure" hidden in an isolated area near Virginia Beach. He described accurately enough the general location but would not or could not pinpoint the exact spot, to everyone's chagrin. The treasure hunters wasted many long hours, back-breaking labor, and finances on a will-o-the-wisp. Among the victims of this lark were his sons, Hugh Lynn and Edgar Evans. One might wonder if the sleeping seer were really asleep or just having a little fun, which would seem unlikely, considering the character of the man.

Another search for buried treasure—that of a Union Army payroll—proved equally futile. And in the series of readings, he changed the cache from gold pieces to silver pieces. Worse still, Union troops were paid in greenbacks, not in coin. These two cases are discussed in detail and make intriguing reading along with others in a timely volume, *The Outer Limits of Edgar Cayce's Power*, written by his two sons.

Sexual Mores

America's inordinate preoccupation with the subject of sex has spawned a rash of sexual Freedomities, Women's Libbers, Playboy philosophers, and assorted pornographers. It has raised profound questions about man-woman relationships: love, home, marriage, the family unit.

The new sex game has eroded our most basic and enduring institutions arrived at by trial and error over the millennia. But it is not really new, for it is as old as man, and every time "free love" has failed as a solid foundation for a society. Edward Gibbon wrote that fallen empires have certain common characteristics, among them promiscuity, corruption, a high standard of living, an over-size military. America has all of them.

Edgar Cayce had something to say about human sexuality—not all of it consistent with the facts as we know them—and he generally takes the conventional view. The male–female relationship represents the positive–negative poles in human-kind—and that is why the sparks sometimes fly. The Law of One, he suggested, applies in sex as it does in religious beliefs. The tenets of the ancient Atlantean Law of One consisted of Our Religion, One State, One Mate, One Home, One God. The decline of the Atlantean empire set in with the decline of sex morality in a rich nation, and corruption in high places and civil war soon followed. The struggle between the Children of the Law of One and the Sons of Belial was underway. It is explored at length in *Edgar Cayce's Story of the Origin and Destiny of Man*.

Of sex Cayce had this to say: " . . . there should be those precautions, understandings, relationships as to how and in what manner there becomes biological urge . . . For it is as from the beginning of puberty the essence of the Creative Forces or energies within the body of the individual. And if such (sex) forces are turned to those channels for the aggrandizement of selfish motives or for the satisfying or the gratifying of . . . emotions, they become destructive; not only in the manner of the offspring but also in the . . . energies of the bodies so producing same." (*Case #826–6*)

No evidence has come to light of any destruction to the body of the offspring. Indeed, biographies reveal that many of the most creative persons were illegitimate. But Cayce may be correct about the energies of the participants. Some artistic people have proclaimed the value of abstinence in sex while in the crucible of creative expression. Their imagination, spontaneity, and drive, they feel, are retained and enhanced.

In the same discourse, Cayce went on to say: "For, to be sure, relationships in the sex are the exercising of the highest emotions in which a physical body may indulge. And *only* in man is there found that such (practices) are used as that of *destruction* to the body-offspring! . . . Those then that besmirch same by over-indulgence besmirch that which is best within themselves. And that should be the key to birth control or sex relations . . ." Medical surveys show that bachelors have more heart attacks and die younger than married men.

"The sex demand of every individual must be gratified in some manner as a portion of the biological urge within the individual . . . It is as natural for there to be sexual relations between man and woman, when drawn together in their regular relations or activities, as it is for the flowers to bloom in the spring, or for the snows to come in the winter."

Is monogamy the best form of home relationship? he

was asked, ". . . monogamy is the best, of course, an indicated from the Scripture itself—One—One! For the union of one should ever be One." (*Case #826-6*) Yet, when asked if sexual intercourse outside marriage is injurious morally and spiritually, he replied: "This must ever be answered from one's own inner self. Those attributes of pro-creation, of the pro-activity in individuals, are from the God-Force itself. The promptings of the inner man must ever be the guide; not from any source may there be given other than, 'Study to show thyself approved unto the God that thou would worship.' As ye would have men do to you, do ye even so to them. In the light of thine own understanding, keep thy body pure, as thou would have others keep their bodies pure. For thy body is the temple of the Living God. Do not desecrate same in thine own consciousness." (*Case #826-2*)

The commitment of marriage, he indicated, is necessary and advisable, ever a help, an advantage. "No soul enters this world by chance, but in order that it may fulfill what it has sought and does seek as its ideal." (*Case #3051*)

The home is the highest of man's achievements in the earth, he said. To one woman he exhorted: "Do make the home the career, for this is the greatest career any soul may make in the earth. To a few it is given to have both a career and a home but the greatest of all careers is the home . . . For this is the nearer of the emblems of what each soul hopes eventually to attain, a heavenly home. Then make thy home as a shadow of a heavenly home." (*Case #5050-1*) ". . . the home is the foundation of the ideals and purposes of the nation. And these should be, these are sacred in the experiences of those that would serve Him wholly and surely." (*Case #3241-1*)

Americans have been led to believe that they can do anything they want in search of pleasure, and this is true. But what they are not told is that they can do anything they want if they are willing to pay the price. And the price is often a high one. Freedom demands self-restraint. Sexual pleasure requires sexual responsibility. The demoralizing affect of the promiscuity of the past decade is now making itself felt in our deteriorating society. It has raised the ugly problems of widespread legal and illegal abortions, suicides, epidemics of venereal disease, broken homes, fatherless children; emotional, financial, psychological and spiritual breakdowns; loneliness in the latter years when youth has been spent and attractiveness depleted. It has been a period in which all the technology of advertising and publicity has been applied to selling sexual excitement. The System has taken the romance out of love and love out of sex, and it's the woman who pays the highest price. They give away their trump card. Sexual liberation has liberated the men of responsibility, while illegitimate births have quadrupled since 1940.

"Nothing is free, least of all sex", writes George Gilder in his thoughtful book, *Sexual Suicide*. "Sex can be cheapened, of course, but then, paradoxically, it becomes extremely costly to the society as a whole. For sex is the life force and cohesive impulse of a people; their very character will be deeply affected by how sexuality is managed, sublimated, denied and propagated." It is love that makes sexual energy a vital force for sustaining psychological, ethical, and communal well-being. Few people want to make a firm commitment to a public utility. Love for the opposite sex and children translates into love for the home, the community that supports them; and faith in the future and the hope for a better society.

Sex can be an entrapment. The present generation in its lack of self-discipline has confused physical sex and true love—the reflection of one's better self seen in some other person, the spiritual bond between two people. Human sexuality is as old as mankind, but the youth of today think they have discovered something new. There is nothing new under the sun, Cayce tritely but truly said, "All has been before."

Soul-birth

One of the vital issues on which Cayce's readings might be helpful has to do with abortion. The important question of the time of entry of the soul into the physical body is crucial in any discussion of the abortion-murder problem. If the fetus is without a soul it is not really human but merely a physical creature; although the potential is there, abortion is not human murder even if it is something akin to it. If the soul is present, it may indeed be premeditated murder.

What does Cayce say? On different occasions he gave different answers. "Where does the soul come from, and how does it enter the physical body?" he was asked. "It is already there; and He breathed into him the breath of life, and he became a living soul," he quotes Genesis. "As the breath, the ether from the forces as come into the body of the human when born breathes the breath of life, (so) it becomes a living soul provided it has reached that developing in the creation where the soul may enter and find the lodging place . . ." (*Case #3744-4*)

On other occasions he said the soul may enter anytime between birth and twenty-four hours after birth. In reading *#457-10*, we find: "It may (enter) at the first moment of breath; it may some hours before birth; it may many hours after birth. This depends on that condition, that environ surrounding the circumstance." He indicates the soul may hover about the fetus before making a final decision in this passage: "It enters either at the first breath physically drawn, or during the first twenty-four hours of cycle activity in a material plane. Not always at the first breath; sometimes there are hours, and there are changes even of personalities as to the seeking to enter." (*Case #2390-2*) What keeps the physical body living until the soul enters? "Spirit! For, the spirit of matter—its source is life, or God, see?" The spirit is the life, he often said.

As for the entry of the soul, apparently it may be at birth or a few hours before or after birth. If true, the fetus prior to that time is not a viable human being. Yet the potential is imminent, the laws of Nature thwarted, life is taken, and the abortion–murder issue remains a risky one indeed.

A childless wife once asked why. Karma, said Cayce; she had abandoned her infant in a Persian incarnation.

Retarded Children

Another question of our times is the problem of imbecilic children. According to Cayce, the soul of the most retarded is capable of grasping—apparently by example and precept or some unknown form of extrasensory perception—far more than is commonly recognized. They should not be put away, he advised, but kept at home and tended with the love and care only parents can give. The cause may be karmic, as this reading indicates:

"Here we find a physical expression of wantoness and selfishness manifested, in the lack of mental, spiritual and physical expression in the present . . . (Mongoloid) The entity turned away from (those who were without hope, who were disturbed in body and mind), the entity turned . . . (to) the enjoying of the appetites in self . . . here we find that the entity is overtaken, and that what the entity has sown he is reaping.

". . . That the soul-consciousness of this entity may become aware of what true abiding love leads individuals (the parents) to do concerning those who are dependent upon others for every care, sow the seed of truth, of hope, of mercy, of kindness, of patience . . . making known by application the truths that 'I am my brother's keeper'."

To some this might appear quite hopeless. Yet there is evidence to support what Cayce had to say. One example is of a speechless teenager, Eva Winter of Denmark. Although markedly retarded, she shows unusual talent as a painter and produces meaningful, artistic pictures. A man in Arizona, while he has a very short attention span, is adept at the piano. The best documented case is that of Nigel Bruce of Britain. A mongoloid, he excelled at woodworking and spent long hours in his shop. At the age of twenty, he wrote a book on the perceptions of a retarded youth, expressing sensitve feelings and great love for his parents, especially his mother. His comprehension of emotional experiences as distinct from mental ones was far beyond expectation.

While the conscious mind may be limited, the subconscious is still at work, Cayce suggested; it is an attribute of the soul, or mind of the soul, he maintained. If true, it may be more cognizant of its environment than we presently suspect.

"For each entity in the earth is what it is because of what it has been! And each moment is dependent upon another moment. So a sojourn in the earth, as indicated, is as a lesson in the school of life and experience." (*Case #2823-3*)

Spirit Communication

On the volatile subject of contacting the departed, Cayce takes contradictory positions. He maintains that communication is within the realm of possibility, but he downgrades mediums in one instance and upgrades them in another.

In case *#140-10* he says, "Love can be sent from one in the spiritual realm to one in the physical world. By themselves, they may gain that close access to the consciousness of the nearness and at-oneness of the individual; but it cannot be done through someone else, such as a medium."

In case *#5756-4*, he takes a different tack. "As may be illustrated in: The message as may be received from the boy just passed into the spirit world, and able through mediumistic forces of someone to communicate to mother, 'All is well. Do not grieve. Do not long for the change.' Such seems to be in the nature of rebuke to a conscious mind when momentous questions . . . might be propounded . . ."

And then he adds: "Rather cultivate that of such

communications, and receive the answer to that of the most profound that may be propounded in any way and manner to those seeking such information. Is such information always true? Always true, so far as the individual has brought self into that attunement as is necessary for the perfect understanding of same.''

If always true, one can only wonder why there is so much inconsistency and contradiction in what mediums have to say. To one individual, Cayce made a biting remark. Why do you want to communicate with Uncle Joe—you didn't pay any attention to him while he was here!

Is communication always possible? he was asked. The answer was Yes and No, for the way and the mood must be prepared—both sender and receiver must be spiritually ready. Communication cannot be forced; it must be desired by both and take place before the departed goes on to other planes of consciousness beyond reach. This may be a matter of hours, days, or years, depending on the development of the individual, the attachment to people, places, or things.

Considering the amount of fraud in this field, one can only be dubious.

Critique of a Life Reading

In 1939, a young, ambitious, energetic man of twenty-six, who prefers to be nameless, received a Life Reading from Edgar Cayce. A natural skeptic, he was in no way interested in religion, psychic phenomena, metaphysics, civic or public affairs. He had never heard of reincarnation. His philosophy of life, if he had one, was a conglomeration of impulses rather than a pattern of principles. He was, in fact, coaxed into requesting the reading of which he had only cursory interest and few expectations.

Now, at age 65, he believes the 38-year-old analysis of himself to be correct behind the realm of pure chance. Although he still disputes parts of it, he believes it has become more and more accurate with the passage of time.

The reading is presented verbatim in its entirety, with comments by the recipient and the facts as known by the author.

(*#2062-1*) This Psychic Reading given by Edgar Cayce at his home on Artic Crescent, Virginia Beach, Va., this 13th day of December, 1939, in accordance with request made by Mr. Zee.

PRESENT
Edgar Cayce; Gertrude Cayce, Conductor;
Gladys Davis, Steno.
READING
(Name of entity)
Born April 11, 1913
in McMinnville, Warren County,
Tennessee.

Time of Reading   Street name and number
10.30 to 11.25 a.m. Eastern Standard   City and State

Mrs. C: You will give the relation of this entity and the universe, and the universal forces; giving the conditions which are as personalities, latent and exhibited in the present life; also the former appearances in the earth plane, giving time, place, and the name, and that in each life which built or retarded the development for the entity; giving the abilities of the present entity, and that to which it may attain, and how. You will answer the questions as I ask them.

Mr. C: Yes—we have the records, we are given the records here of that entity now known as or called . . . In giving the interpretations of the records here, these are chosen with the desire that this be a helpful experience for the entity. While there are many qualities in the characteristics of the entity that may be lauded, there are those also, those tendencies to which reference may be made, and counsel given for the correcting of same, so that much good, many helpful influences may arise in the experience of the entity in this present sojourn.

(Cayce has never been accused of flattery. On the contrary, the readings more often place the emphasis on the vices than on the virtues; they seem most concerned with the spiritual growth not the material growth of the individual.)

As indicated from astrological aspects as well as material sojourns, the entity is destined to be in contact with many varied types of individuals; peoples in and from all walks of life and experiences. Thus there may come to the entity the opportunity for sowing the seeds of the spirit of truth and love. Thus may the entity develop and grow to become an influence, a force, a power for good—which is the purpose for each soul's entering material experiences.

(Here Cayce scores a series of hits and a miss. The entity did come in "contact with many varied types of individuals". When World War II came along, he went into the Army and served three years in this country, France, Germany, and the Philippines, observing how the people lived, their cultures and ways of life. Later, he resided in a half-dozen states as a store manager, buyer, merchandise manager, claims agent, insurance investigator, law enforcement officer. He has dealt with criminals, lawyers, judges, con men, clergymen, saints and devils. The "opportunity for sowing the seeds of the spirit of truth and love", was ample. A world traveler, tapes of his talks and tv-radio interview shows reveal that he has a high sense of justice and an inclination to bring a message and espouse a cause.

(Cayce may be right about his influence and force for good, but "a power for good" is much too sweeping a word, he believes. It connotes a national reputation, which is not the case.)

Yet to become a sower of the seed of truth, and the spirit, and love, these must of necessity be manifested and a part of the purpose of the individual himself—if these would bring that result which is possible, and which is to be desired by each entity, each soul.

(As always, Cayce put the final burden on the entity, and these general exhortations have to at least a reasonable degree been accomplished by the recipient.)

In the astrological aspects we find Mars, Venus, Jupiter and Uranus as those influences which exert an influence—through the varied experiences or environs—upon the tendencies or inclinations in the reactions of the entity to conditions, peoples, or things. For instance, in Mars we find the inclination for the entity to be self-centered; not in the personage of such a great selfishness, but rather inclined to be DETERMINED to have self's own way, even though the entity may be convinced or shown that other manners, other ways might be better.

(At the time of the reading, Cayce was partly correct. The entity's philosophy was much like that of the umpire, he says: once a bad call was made he felt compelled to stick with it, even though he knew he had made a mistake. Happily, this concept is no longer true for the man.)

There is the inclination or tendency also under such conditions, even though thwarted in the activities, to discuss or think about such things.

(Here Cayce seems to have been reading his mind, for he sometimes used the umpire illustration in defense of an untenable position.)

Remember that silence often is golden, and determine in self to better acquaint thine own understanding with ALL PHASES of whatever the problem or condition may be. This is inclined to give the tendency to become too much of a one-track mind, or when a purpose is before the entity—as to the manner or the means of attaining same—if there is a conclusion drawn, others are not always, or other circumstances, or other conditions about the entity given full or due consideration . . .

(Again, Cayce was right, although today this person considers all phases almost to the point of being somewhat indecisive in his actions while being rather dogmatic in his views.)

This finds expression in that which is oft called or termed a nervous disposition, a tendency to be erratic. This is more oft, as it grows upon a body, tended to be used as an excuse—and such may undermine the abilities even of such a one as this entity in accomplishing the good, or expanding or excelling in the manner it should.

(Cayce could hardly have been more correct in his use of the words "nervous disposition" and "erratic". But he was wrong at the time about these being used as excuses. The individual was not aware of and admitted to no such shortcomings. Today, he knows they are true, and to his chagrin he sometimes uses them as an explanation for his impulsive words or actions—to himself rather than to others, he says.)

Read more oft the law of love, that is a part of thy daily life. Grow in spiritual understanding that thy mental and thy physical manifestations in thy relationships to others and conditions may be tempered with that mercy, that justice, the kindness, that patience as ye would have thy Lord, thy God, thy Savior have with thee.

(The phraseology is typical Cayce, common in many readings. Nevertheless, this person has for many years been devoted to spiritual and religious matters, has never been accused of being unkind or unjust, and says that love is indeed the answer to most of the world's problems; if only there were more of it. He admittedly is short on patience.)

From the influences in Venus we find a sentiment, a "letting off" of emotions through same at times. To be sure, all phases of urges from astrological or material sojourns are merely inclinations, tendencies, and the entity does not necessarily have to react.

(Normally quiet, amiable, and self-contained, Mr. Zee can at times become emotional and volatile, especially when subjects of justice, morals or principles arise. He is extremely sensitive to many of these and inclined to erupt suddenly.)

Hence that injunction—study more thoroughly. Delight in the law of the Lord; meditate in same day and night; and THEN in all phases of the experience ye will be happy, harmonious, AND successful in every phase of thy relationships. Remember, too, that as ye do it unto the least of thy acquaintances, thy associates—yea, the casual passerby—ye are doing it unto thy Lord, thy God.

(He appears to have fulfilled the injunctions and is reasonably happy and harmonious. But Cayce failed when he said he would be successful. The man says he is willing to pit his failures against anyone's; his wheel of fortune has often turned in reverse in the past.)

For thou, veritably, believeth that in Him ye move and have thy being. Then act in that way and manner by the more oft seeking to know what He would have thee do. Thus ye will find that thy will, thy temperament, will become more and more able to be gentle, patient, kind, long-suffering, with brotherly love; and these are indeed the fruits of the spirit. And they that manifest such in their daily life walk close with Him in every way.

(He does manifest these "fruits of the spirit", but he's not so certain that all who do so "walk close with Him in every way". Yet, some metaphysician might say, his impatience and emotionalism stand in the way.)

In Jupiter we find the affluence, or the tendencies for the dreams of great things and great associations that are or may be a party of the activities, if those purposes and intents as pointed out are manifested in the daily life of the entity.

(The reading is right about the dreams of great things but short on the realization of them. The subject believes his intents are beyond question, and he is probably correct. Those who know him do not doubt his sincerity of purpose. An idealist and perfectionist, he has for many years dedicated himself to various crusades of all work and no pay. He says he almost invariably "worked for political losers, which is why we have such bad government!")

From Uranus we find those tendencies for the extremes, and to dwell upon conditions, things or activities; sometimes to that extent that the oneness of the self becomes over-powering.

(An extremist he is, always with an eye to the future for the common man. A liberal reformer, he might aptly be called a conservative left-radical in socio–economic–political matters. He says he has never understood the line about the oneness of the self becoming overpowering, and doesn't believe it's true. Issue oriented, he is not overly ambitious or self-seeking. Modest, basically shy, his ego rarely shows.)

Hence, again the injunction: look upon all phases; for there is the mental, the material, and the spiritual, and these are the phases of man's reaction and man's activity. Do not apply the law of the spiritual in material things, nor the material in spiritual things. Remember that mind is the builder and the spirit giveth life. And as ye use and dwell upon such, be sure thy ideal is in Him.

(The subject asserts he has never comprehended the meaning of "Do not apply the law of the spiritual in material things, nor the material in spiritual things". If spiritual laws are so limited, he insists, they are not of much use in a material world. Deeply spiritual himself, he is convinced that "mind is the builder and that the spirit giveth life".)

As to the appearances in the earth, these we find quite varied in their relationships to those activities that may be a part of the entity's experience, and yet they indicate those fields or trends of activity in which greater harmony and greater abilities may be aroused to action. Before this we find the entity was in the land of its present nativity, and during those periods of turmoils and strife—in that called the Civil War. The entity was among the southern contingents, acting in the capacity of what is called the commissionary, or one providing provisions for the handling of those who served in the capacity of soldiers. Thus we find the entity met many of those disturbing conditions, many of those in activities that brought the weighty problems of considering manners and means of distribution, as well as those influences from which resources might be obtained.

(There is no way of proving or disproving a past incarnation, but this one does have some supportive circumstantial evidence. In his youth, the subject was fascinated with Civil War history and an avid reader of it. His background in wholesale-retail merchandising and distribution fits in well; in World War II he was in charge of a regimental post office.)

The name then was Carl Brickner. In the experience the entity gained, for the sincerity of purpose was manifested in the manner in which the entity conducted himself. But that singleness of direction in the present needs to be tempered with the better concept of all phases, and the dependencies of all manners of influences in the present relationships.

(After extensive effort and research, no trace has been found of Carl Brickner, and the Brickners are a small clan. Unhappily, Confederate Army records, fragmented in the fire of Richmond when the city was under siege, are far from complete. The subject does exude a certain seriousness and impulsive urgency in the tasks before him but is not regarded as being doggedly tenacious.)

Also there are the inclinations, the tendencies, the abilities of the entity in the present to serve in the capacity of cooperating, coordinating with great corporations—or where consignments may be made or where there needs to be considered the activity of many various phases of man's needs and man's desires as to man's relationships. But temper these ever with the spiritual import.

(Cooperative and coordinating he is, but he is not certain of the meaning of "where consignments may be made". An advocate for the little man, he has long been interested in the field of social concerns.)

Before that we find the entity was in that called the Roman land, when there were the attempts more for the correlating of the Grecian and Roman power, or the tempering of the Roman power with the Grecian upbuilding or Grecian culture. Thus the entity's activities were given in those offices in which there was a study made as to the needs of the one and the fitness of the other for its injection into the activities of the peoples in various forms and manners. The name then was Helceon, and we find that the entity met and consulted with those peoples in all walks of life; those who would forward the drama, music, games, physical activities, or the learning and art and literature of all natures.

(The Roman–Grecian period of the fifᵗh century B.C. has no appeal to him whatever. He is mildly interested in the arts, and in drama and fiction only if they have "something important to say". His interests are in history, politics, economics, religion, literature and those things that will improve the lot of the plain people.)

Thus we find that the entity in the present is capable of meeting all kinds and characters of individuals, and able to adjust self to the considerations of the needs of all of these. (True) Thus there may come, in the present experience, the conditions, the circumstance, the opportunities for the applying and the use of these tendencies within the experience and in the relationships. (True to some degree) Temper these, also, with those things that bear the fruit of the spirit, and SOW these seed in thy daily activities with others in all walks of thy experience. (This he has apparently done.)

Before that we find the entity was in the Atlantean land, when there was the exodus of the peoples to the Egyptian land. The entity was among those leaders of the peoples who entered into Egypt; and considered among the counselors of same, with great efficiency and ability in choosing individuals for active service in relationships to the State, or to the offices for the greater good, or the common good of the whole—or of groups.

(The subject regards prehistoric Egypt and Atlantis as two of the most fascinating periods and is well informed on them. A reincarnationist, he suspects that his interest in public affairs stems from this era, around 10,300 B.C. Somewhat cynical today, he says, "A pessimist is an informed optimist.")

In the Egyptian land this caused quite a disturbance to the entity, owing to the rebellions and the attempts of the Atlanteans to take advantage of the situation to establish themselves the greater, and the recall of the

Priest. For the entity, then as Zeutex, became greatly disturbed because of embitterments which arose between the entity and the Priest. Yet eventually, through the deeper considerations of self and its peoples, there was the absorbing of the ideals and ideas of the Priest, or the turning of the ideas into ideals, through the seeking to comprehend, to understand and then to practically apply the tenets of "The Lord thy God is One".

(The Egyptian Priest was Ra Ta, supposedly the entity Edgar Cayce in a past incarnation. The subject, at first an unbeliever in the work of Cayce, did eventually come to accept it, with some reservations, in broad, general terms. As for the ideas and ideals, he is persuaded they are of the highest order.)

As to the abilities of the entity in the present, then, and that to which it may attain and how: Take those warnings, those admonitions that have been indicated and meditate upon them—through those channels and through those ways and understandings that have been given. Know the 30th of Deuteronomy; the 14th, 15th, 16th and 17th of St. John as the pattern of thy life, of thy relationships to others.

(The Cayce readings recommend meditation again and again, but the man confesses he has never had any success with it. He is willing to accept the efficacy of meditation for those who can achieve it, but believes they are few. Some who have been "meditating" for years confide that they too have had no success at it. In the 30th chapter of Deuteronomy, Moses exhorts the Jews to obey the commandments. In St. John, Jesus speaks to the Disciples of love, obedience, His departure and return. Both texts were often recommended by Cayce, and therefore were not for this entity alone.)

In fields of service where there are those opportunities to greatly aid others by the distribution of things and conditions needed that pertain to the creating of a better environment for all peoples, will be the outlet for a material service. Let not thy left hand know what thy right hand doeth.

(Cayce's prediction is in very general terms, but the

man did spend twenty years in the field of merchandising and has worked for many social causes. He
had little or no interest in either at the time of the
reading, he says. He is not sure of the meaning of "Let
not they left hand know what thy right hand doeth".
Presumably he is not to pat himself on the back.)

Q. Should I remain with my present firm or make the
change that is contemplated?

A. As we find, the present associations offer a greater
opportunity for a broader service in those directions indicated. But if the change is accepted, because of other
environmental circumstances, then indeed study to
show thyself approved—not to thy handservant nor to
thy employer so much as to God!

(Here Cayce is off the mark, assuming the man had a
specific change in mind, which he did not. He simply
disliked his job, found it boring and unchallenging, and
wanted to make almost any kind of change. He was
seeking advice that he did not get. Four years later he
left the company and went into the Army. After World
War II, he found himself back in the merchandising
field but in more responsible positions.)

Q. For what vocation am I best adapted at present?
What weak points in my personality should I develop?

A. This has been indicated, and there only needs to be
the study and the analysis, and then the suggestions applied as to correct the weaknesses in the manner indicated.

Q. Just what business plans should I make for the
future?

A. MEDITATE, MEDITATE in the law of the Lord!
And then use that which is in hand!

We are through for the present.

(The subject asserts he long ago learned to use that
which is in hand, mainly because there is usually
nothing else to be done. As for meditation, he finds he is
often unable to empty his mind, a prerequisite.)

At this point in the march of time the reading appears
to be amazingly accurate, and Mr. Zee, who is in ex-

cellent health, has perhaps another ten to twenty years
to go.

On Reincarnation

At the Second Annual Congress of the Association
for Research and Enlightenment in June of 1933, Edgar
Cayce gave a lengthy reading on the subject of the continuity of life for the thirty-five inquisitive members
present in Virginia Beach. The discourse is here reported
verbatim so that the reader may judge for himself its
value and credibility.

Gertrude Cayce: You will give at this time a comprehensive discourse on reincarnation. If the soul returns to the earth through a succession of appearances,
you will explain why this is necessary or desirable, and
will clarify through explanation the laws governing such
returns. You will answer the questions which will be
asked on this subject.

Edgar Cayce: Yes. In giving even an approach to the
subject sought here, it is well that there be given some
things that may be accepted as standards from which
conclusions—or where parallels—may be drawn, that
there may be gathered in the minds of those who would
approach same some understanding, some concrete
examples, that may be applied in their own individual
experience.

Each soul that enters, then, must have had an impetus
from some beginning that is of the Creative Energy, or
of a first cause. What, then, was—or is—the first cause?
For if there be law pertaining to the first cause it must be
an unchangeable law, and is—IS—as 'I am that I am!'
For this is the basis from which one would reason: The
first cause was that the created would be the companion
for the Creator; that it, the creature, would—through
its manifestations in the activity of that given unto the
creature—show itself to be not only worthy of but companionable to the Creator.

Hence, every form of life that man sees in a material
world is an essence or manifestation of the Creator; not

the Creator, but a manifestation of a first cause—and in its own sphere, its own consciousness of its activity in that plane or sphere. Hence, as man in this material world passes through there are the manifestations of the attributes that the consciousness attributes to, or finds coinciding with, that activity which is manifested; hence becomes then as the very principle of the law that would govern an entrance into a manifestation.

Then a soul, the offspring of a Creator entering into a consciousness that became a manifestation in any plane or sphere of activity, given that free will for its use of those abilities, qualities, conditions in its experience, demonstrates, manifests, shows forth that it reflects in its activity towards that first cause. Hence, in the various spheres that man sees that are demonstrated, manifested in and before self even in a material word, all forces, all activities, are a manifestation. Then that which would be the companionable, the at-oneness with, the ability to be one with, becomes necessary for the demonstration or manifestation of those attributes in and through all force, all demonstration, in a sphere.

Because an atom, a matter, a form is changed does not mean that the essence, the source or the spirit of it has changed; only in its form of manifestation, and *not* in its relation with the first cause. That man reaches that consciousness in the material plane of being aware of what he does about or with the consciousness of the knowledge, the intelligence, the first cause, makes or produces that which is known as the entering into the first cause, principles, basis, or the essence, that there may be demonstrated in that manifested that which gains for the soul, for the entity, that which would make the soul an acceptable companion to the Creative Energy, Creative Influence. See?

As to how, where, when, and what produces the entrance into a material manifestation of an entity, a soul: In the beginning was that which set in motion that which is seen in manifested form with the laws governing same. The inability of destroying matter, the ability of each force, each source of power or contact—as it meets in its various forms—produces that which is a manifestation in a particular sphere. This may be seen in those elements used in the various manifested ways of preparing for man, in many ways, those things that bespeak of the laws that govern man's relationship to the first cause, or God.

Then this is the principle: Like begets like. Those things that are positive and negative forces combine to form in a different source or different manifestation, the combinations of which each element, each first principle manifested, has gained from its associations—in its activities—that which has been brought to bear by self or that about it, to produce that manifestation.

Hence man, the crowning of all manifestations in a material world—a causation world—finds self as the cause and the product of that he (man), with those abilities given, has been able to produce or demonstrate or manifest from that he, the soul, has gained, does gain in the transition, the change, the going forward that and being of that from which he came. Periods, times, places: That which is builded, each in its place, each in its time.

This is shown to man in the elemental world about him. Man's consciousness of that about him is gained through that he, man, does about the knowledge of that he is, as in relation to that from which he came and towards which he is going. Hence, in man's analysis and understanding of himself, it is as well to know from whence he came as to know whither he is going.

Ready for questions.

Q. What is meant by inequality of experience? Is it a strong argument for reincarnation?

A. Considering that which has just been presented, isn't it the same argument?

Q. Is experience limited to this earth plane?

A. As each entity, each soul in the various consciousnesses passes from one to another, it—the soul—becomes conscious of that about self in that sphere to which it, the entity, the soul, attains in a materially manifested way or manner. Hence the entity develops

through the varied spheres of the earth and its solar
system, and the companions of varied experiences in
that solar system or spheres of development or activity,
as in some ways accredited correctly to the planetary influences in an experience. The entity develops through
those varied spheres.

Hence the sun, the moon, the stars, the position in the
heavens or in all of the hosts of the solar systems that
the earth occupies—all have their influence in the same
manner. This is a very crude illustration but very
demonstrative; that the effect of a large amount of any
element would attract a compass. Drawn to! Why?
Because of the influence of which the mind element of a
soul, an entity, has become conscious!

A soul, an entity is as real as a physical entity, and is
as subject to laws as the physical body is subject to the
laws in a material world and the elements thereof! Does
fire burn the soul or the physical body? Yet self may
cast self into a fire element by doing that the soul knows
to be wrong! What would make a wrong and a right? A
comparison of that the soul knows its consciousness to
be in accord or contrariwise with, in relation to that
which gave it existence.

Q. Are not transferred memories misappropriated by individuals and considered to be personal experiences?

A. Personal experiences have their influence upon the
inner soul, while disincarnate entities that may be earth-
bound or that may be heaven-bound may influence the
thought of an entity or a mind. But, who gives the law
to have an element to influence, whether from self or
from another? That same as from the beginning: The
will of the soul that it may be one with the first cause. In
the material, the mental, and the spiritual experience of
many souls, many entities, it has been found that there
be those influences that *do* have their effect upon the
thought of those who would do this or that. Who gives
it? Self!

Just as it is when an entity, a body, fills its mind
(mentally, materially) with those experiences that
bespeak of those things which add to the carnal forces

of an experience, just so does the mind become the builder throughout. And the mental mind or physical mind becomes carnally directed! The mind is the builder ever, whether in the spirit or in the flesh. If one's mind is filled with those things that bespeak of the spirit, that one becomes spiritual-minded. As we may find in a material world: Envy, strife, selfishness, greediness, avarice are the children of *man*! Long-suffering, kindness, brotherly love, good deeds are the children of the spirit of light. Choose ye (as it has ever been given) whom ye will serve.

This is not beggaring the question! As individuals become abased or possessed, are their thoughts guided by those in the borderland? Certainly! If allowed to be! But he that looks within is higher, for the spirit knoweth the Spirit of its Maker, and the children of same are as given. And, "My Spirit beareth witness with thy spirit," saith He who giveth life! What *is* life? A manifestation of the first cause—God!

Q. Explain, in the light of reincarnation, the cycle of development towards maturity in individuals.

A. As an individual in any experience, in any period, uses that of which it (the soul or entity) is conscious in relation to the laws of the Creative Force, so does that soul, that entity develop towards—what? A companionship with the Creative Influence! Hence karma, to those disobeying—by making for self that which would be as the towers of Babel, or as the city of Gomorrah, or as the fleshpots of Egypt, or as the caring for those influences in the experience that satisfy or gratify self without thought of the effect upon that which it has in its own relation to the first cause! Hence to many this becomes as the stumbling block.

It is as was given by Him, "I am the way. No man approaches the Father but by me." But, does a soul crucify the flesh even as He, when it finds within itself that it must work out its own salvation in a material world, by entering and re-entering that there may be made manifest that consciousness in the soul that would make it a companion with the Creator?

Rather is the law of forgiveness made of effect in thine experience through Him that would stand in thy stead; for He is the Way, that Light ever ready to aid when there is the call upon—and the trust of the soul in—that first cause!

Has it not been given that there is an influence in the mind, the thought of man, from the outside? Then, would those who have lost their way become the guides and both fall in the ditch? Or would the soul trust in the Way and the Light, and seek in that way that there may be shown the light? What caused the first influences in the earth that brought selfishness? The desire to be as gods; in that rebellion became the order of the mental forces in the soul; and sin entered.

Q. What is the strongest argument against reincarnation?

A. That there is the law of cause and effect in *material* things. But the strongest argument against reincarnation is also, turned over, the strongest argument for it; as in *any* principle, when reduced to its essence. For the *law* is set—and it happens! though a soul may will itself *never* to reincarnate, but must burn and burn and burn—or suffer and suffer and suffer! For the heaven and hell is built by the soul!

The companionship in God is being one with Him; and the gift of God is being conscious of being one with Him, yet apart from Him—or one with yet apart from the Whole.

Q. What is the strongest argument for reincarnation?

A. Just as given. Just turn it over; or as we have outlined.

We are through for the present. (*Case #5753–1*)

If reincarnation is a fact, although unprovable, it explains the child prodigy, the genius, the talented, the deformed and the handicapped.

On Health and Well-Being

In speaking of ancient times, Cayce once made an extravagant claim. "What was the length of life then? Nearly a thousand years. What is your life today? May it not be just as He had given, just as He indicated to those peoples, just as He did to the law giver, just as He did to David—first from a thousand years to a hundred and twenty, then to eighty? Why? Why? The sin of man is his desire for self-gratification.

"What nations of the earth today vibrate to those things that they have and are creating in their own land, their own environment? Look to the nations where the span of life has been extended from sixty to eighty-four years. You will judge who is serving God. These are judgments." (*Case #3976–29*)

No nation of record has average longevity for its inhabitants of eighty-four years, and no known nation in the common use of that word even approaches the figure, although some do not know or do not report such statistics. As for man living a thousand years in olden times, there is no way of crediting or discrediting such an assertion; at best it seems highly improbable.

According to United Nations tables compiled by the World Health Organization, socialist Sweden ranks first in longevity with an average of 72.07 years for males and 77.65 years for females. Following close behind are Norway, Iceland, Holland, and Denmark. The U.S.

ranks far down with 68.2 years for men and 75.9 years for women. Russian males, heavy drinkers, on the average live to 68 and females to 76 years of age. But the Soviets claim to have the world's oldest living people, and it may be true. *Tass* reports there are 19,300 citizens over the age of 100 years.

The largest body of centenarians exists in the Caucasian Mountains of the U.S.S.R.—some 5000—of whom half live in the Azerbaijan Republic. That is 84 persons per 100,000 population living to be 100 or more. Many live to 150 years, and two reached 154 and 165 years. Ethnically, they are Azerbaijanans, Georgians, Russians, Armenians, Jews; most were married with large families. They attribute their long lives to "freedom, the absence of worry, and useful work".

If we define "nation", as does Webster's, as not exclusively a country or state, but as a "tribe or federation of tribes", or as a "a territorial division containing a body of people", we have a different and more complex situation. The Hunza people of mountainous West Pakistan often live to 100 or more years in vigorous physical and mental health. Vegetarians, they are light eaters of fruits, grains and organically grown vegetables. A friendly, tranquil, religious·people living in harmony, sickness is rare, and crime, cancer, premature heart disease, high or low blood pressure are virtually unknown. Their greatest asset appears to be peacefulness. Unfortunately, no record of their longevity is available, but it must be very high. In 1944, the year of Cayce's reading, Hunza was an independent kingdom, not becoming a part of West Pakistan until 1947.

In Ecuador, the Vilcambama tribe of a remote valley live well beyond the age of 100 and still work and enjoy good health. Of a population of 819 in 1973, 28 were between 85 and 120 years of age. South American doctors attribute their old age to their serenity, with possible contributing factors of an even, year-round temperature of 68 degrees, a vegetarian diet, four centuries of peace. And the men smoke two-three packs of cigarettes a day.

Why the relatively short life of Americans? There are a number of explanations. The infant mortality rate is comparatively high—number 14 in the world of nations table, the doctor-patient ratio ranks in 8th place, in literacy, 14th place. The diet is rich in fats and Americans eat too much. The pace of life is fast and the competitive drive intense. As Cayce so often emphasized, and psychosomatic medicine now corroborates, our spiritual and emotional-mental health is often the cause of our physical health, good or bad it may be. America is Number One militarily but it is 20th in life expectancy. It is also Number One when the mortician presents his bill—"O, Death, here is thy sting."

The Cayce readings stress again and again that human life on earth is but one sojourn among many, that the immortality of the soul is a fact, that terrestrial and celestial experiences are for the spiritual growth of the entity—the real purpose in life. The mystery of death is but the transition from one plane of awareness to another in the solar system, for "*the earth is only an atom in the universe of worlds! . . .*" (Emphasis EC's in all cases.)

"And with error (entities) entered that as called *death*, which is only a transition—or (passing) through God's other door—into that realm where the entity has builded in its manifestations as related to the knowledge and activity respecting the law of the universal influence . . . Death in the material plane is passing through the outer door into a consciousness in the . . . activities that partakes of what the entity or soul has done with its spiritual truth in its manifestations . . ." (*Case #5749-3*)

Such claims can be neither proved or disapproved, but some evidence has recently come to light. Dr. Stanislav Grof, a Czech-born psychiatrist who was on the faculty of Johns Hopkins School of Medicine, and now at the Esalen Institute, has been experimenting with psychedelic drugs to ease the psychological pain of dying for terminal patients. After 3500 tests he has observed some strange results.

"Death," he says, "instead of being seen as the ultimate end of everything and a step into nothingness, appears suddenly as a transition into a different type of existence for those who undergo the destruction—rebirth—cosmic—unity experience. The idea of possible continuity of consciousness beyond physical death becomes much more plausible than the opposite. The patients who have transcendental experiences develop a rather deep belief in the ultimate cosmic unity of all creation and experience themselves as part of it without regard to the situation they are facing."

The evidence is impressive but not conclusive, since it is purely subjective. Without suggestion or coaching, terminal patients with backgrounds from atheism to church-every-Sunday gain a sense of an alternate reality that may be totally foreign to them. Significantly, there is a striking correspondence between this kind of reality and the concepts of Christianity, Hinduism, Buddhism, Taoism and the works of mystics throughout history. Dr. Grof is knowledgeable in this vast theology and literature. Cautiously, however, he concludes, "Whether these are valid insights into the nature of reality, or are merely merciful delusions, I don't think we can say for certain."

More brain-rattling is the claim of Swedish Dr. Nils-Olof Jacobson. In his volume, *Life After Death*, he asserts that the human soul weighs about three-quarters of an ounce! He obtained his statistic by placing terminal cancer patients and their beds on highly sensitive scales to record their weight immediately before and after death. His apparatus showed a weight loss of 21 grams. He also submits that the departing soul does not realize it has separated from its material body, and that the body continues eating, drinking and carrying on all the normal functions during the transitory period.

Cayce did not touch on the last point, but he does sustain the prior one: ". . . many an individual has remained in that called death for what ye call *years* without realizing it was dead! The feelings, the desires for what ye call appetites are changed or not aware (of) at all. The ability to communicate is that which usually disturbs or worries others.'' (*Case #1472–2*) Cayce was speaking of the departed soul, Jacobson of the remaining physical body. Intriguing as their claims are, they are nevertheless beyond proof at this time.

Psychiatrist Elizabeth Kubler-Ross, author of *On Death and Dying*, is convinced that when the physical body dies the psychic life goes on. "There is an experience of floating out of the body", her research shows, in which the "dying person perceives what is happening to his or her corpse" and the "heroic attempts" to resuscitate it. Returnees are never again afraid to die, she says. Dr. Raymond Moody of the University of Virginia came to similar conclusions.

How to live longer? Cayce was asked many times and had a lot to say on the subject. To one woman who inquired, How can I best prepare for old age? he answered, "By preparing for the present. Let age only ripen thee. For one is ever just as young as the heart and the purpose. Keep sweet. Keep friendly. Keep loving, if ye would keep young." (*Case #3420–1*)

To another, he said: "Then, keep that attitude of constructive, creative forces within self. For all healing of every nature must arise within the self. For there is the ability within the physical body to re-create or reproduce itself, as well as the activities for assimilating that from which the re-creation is to be brought about." (*Case #1663–1*)

Again: "For, as we have indicated, the body renews itself according to the mental attitude it holds toward ideals, and in the light of the application of relationships to others. And this applies as well in the relationships to self." (*Case #2081–2*)

The readings consistently emphasize the importance of psychosomatic medicine, the affect of the mental-emotional state on the physical well-being. "Everything that the body has by thought and by action has (*sic*) been created in the body itself. If a perfect balance is kept in the body itself, the expression of thought carries on the forces in the system to perform any of the functioning of the body.'' (*Case #2483-1*)

Science now knows that attitudes effect longevity. Two internationally known cardiologists have recently come up with a theory on the cause of heart attacks, corroborating what Cayce has to say. After fifteen years of experimentation, they found certain traits of the human personality conducive to seizures: aggressiveness, impatience, explosiveness, guilt feelings; hard driving, high achieving, overly ambitious people who don't mind bull-dozing others aside. The mental-emotional state, not eating, drinking, or social habits, is the chief culprit. Alarmingly, over half of Americans fall into this category.

Cayce explained it this way: "In every physical being the whole body is made up of atomic forces, with the mind of each atom, as it is built, supervised by the whole mental mind of the body; an atom of the body is a whole universe in itself." (*Case #137*) "There is nothing outside of self half so fearful as that which may be builded or brewed within self's own mental and material being." (*Case #1928*)

Again and again he warned of hate, anger, anxiety, self-condemnation. All illness comes from sin, he said, the transgression of some spiritual law—love, patience, fairness, understanding. "For the body is indeed the Temple of the Living God," he told one person. "What have you dragged into this Temple?"

When the Nazarene brought the message of love, did He have physical as well as moral reasons for doing so?

Smoking and Drinking

What did Cayce say of our most popular vices? The questions were asked many times, and the answers are at variance to total abstinence. While emphasizing moderation, he makes some significant distinctions.

To a man age 59 who asked, "If smoking is not particularly harmful to the extent that I indulge, is it best that I smoke a pipe or cigarettes?" he answered,

"Smoking in moderation for this body would be help-ful. To excess it's very harmful. The smoking of ciga-rettes is better than most types." (*Case #3539–1*)

A 55-year-old woman wanted to know, "Would smoking of cigarettes in any way be beneficial to my body; if so, what brand and how many a day?" His answer was: "The nicotine for the body would supply a poison that would counter-balance some of the disturb-ances in the system. Three to five a day would be cor-rect. This does not necessarily mean that these would be inhaled, but the brand that is of the purer tobacco is the better." Question: "Which brands are the pure tobac-co?" Answer: "Virginia Ovals and (cigarettes) of such natures." (*Case #303–23*) Since these are both physical readings, the inquirers evidentially had some ailment, as did this man who was told: "Smoking in moderation will be helpful to the body. The best brands, we would find, are those that are of the purer tobacco that are not either toasted or mixed with foreign conditions. Those known as or called Piedmonts are the better." (*Case #1131–2*)

The readings were all given in the 1930's and 40's, and the brands he mentioned have long expired. During this period he made what might be a highly significant remark. "Tobacco in moderation, as all stimulants, is not so harmful. However, over-acidity or over-alkalinity causes same to become detrimental." (*Case # 462–6*) Other readings point out that most people are over-acid.

Some claim that smoking is a depressant, not a stimulant. But a recent British report sustains Cayce's comment that very moderate smoking is not harmful. Yet, as Cayce once complained, man is seldom mod-erate. Three to five cigarettes a day is next to not smoking at all. Before the advent of the filter, "tar" content ran as high as 29 mgs and nicotine 1.8 per cigarette, as some do today. Filter brands now run as low as 1 mg tar and 0.1 mg nicotine. The average popular low-content brands contain around 10 mgs tar and 0.8 mgs nicotine. In other words, translated into

Cayce's terms, three to five cigarettes a day would be the equivalent of eight to twelve medium, low-count, popular brand smokes now on the counters.

Not only the U.S. Surgeon General's report—"Cigarette Smoking is Dangerous to Your Health"—refutes Cayce. So does a 1973 study by the U.S. Public Health Service. "Pipe and cigar smokers in the United States as a group experience mortality rates from lung cancer and emphysema that are slightly higher than those of non-smokers. The typical cigar smoker smokes fewer than five cigars a day, and the typical pipe smoker smokes less than twenty pipefuls a day. Most pipe and cigar smokers report that they do not inhale the smoke. Those who do inhale, inhale infrequently and only slightly. As a result, the harmful effects of cigar and pipe smoking appear to be largely limited to increased death rates from cancer at those sites which are exposed to the smoke of these products."

In sum, the report says cigar smokers get as many mouth cancers as do cigarette smokers. Cancer of the larynx hits all heavy smokers equally, also. And the rate for cancer of the esophagus is about the same. But these rare diseases account for only five percent of U.S. cancers among men. Compared with non-smokers, cigar smokers die up to three times as often from lung cancer; pipe smokers, up to four times as often, and cigarette smokers up to 23 times as often as non-smokers. The difference is attributed to the amount smoked and inhaling habits.

Cayce may be right about very moderate smoking and not inhaling, but wrong about cigarettes being better than pipes and cigars.

"Have personal vices (such) as tobacco and whiskey any influence on one's health or longevity?" a 79-year-old man asked.

. . . "you are suffering from the use of some of these in the present," Cayce replied, "but it is over-indulgence. In moderation these are not too bad, but man so seldom will be moderate. Or, as most say, those who even indulge will make themselves pigs, but we naturally are pigs when there is over-indulgence. This, of course, makes for conditions which are to be met. For what one sows, that must one reap. This is unchangeable law." (*Case #5233–1*)

He took a dim view of hard liquor, except for medicinal purposes, but recommended the light wines— Tokay, Port, Sauterne. "Wine is good for all, if taken alone or with black or brown bread. Not with meats so much as with just bread. This may be taken between meals or as a meal; but not too much—and just once a day. Red wine only." (*Case #462–6*) Sauterne is a white, not a red wine.

As for carbonated drinks, Cayce referred to them as "slop".

In his book, *How to Wine Your Way to Good Health*, Herbert Baus describes wine as a near-perfect food, beneficial to the nervous system, the heart, the respiratory system, weight reducing. His thoroughly researched volume maintains moderate wine drinkers outlive teetotalers.

Coffee with Cream?

According to the Cayce readings, it's not the food we eat but the combinations that are so harmful. Do not take milk or cream in coffee or in tea, they advise. Either may be taken separately at the same meal, but mixed together they become one of the foods that are acid-producing.

Said Cayce: ". . . the combination of the acids—or the tannic forces, the chicory, or the properties that are the food values to the digestive forces—becomes disturbing when combined outside of the body. However, if milk and coffee are taken at the same meal—but not combined before they are taken—the gastric juices flowing from even the salivary glands in the mouth . . . change the activity so that the food values of both are taken by the system, in the activity through the alimentary canal." (*Case #1073–1*)

Little came out of modern scientific laboratories to sustain or refute such a contention until 1974. But an intriguing, 100-year-old study from Europe had something pithy to say on the subject. For whatever it may be worth, we quote:

"Milk is undeniably wholesome and nutritious. Milk and coffee taken separately, not to interfere with each other in the stomach, are excellent; but, what is remarkable, when mixed and taken together they constitute a new composition which is absolutely indigestible . . ." So reports the Société Impériale et Centrale d'Agriculture de France in 1869.

The Society explained its wisdom this way: "Now the infusion of coffee is rich in tannin, hence its mixture with milk has the immediate result of transforming the caseous part and the albumen that it contains into a kind of leather, undecomposable and indigestible, like that made in a tan pit. The composition thus produced remains in the stomach until new aliments come to displace and force it through the lower orifice of the stomach into the intestines. The sugar and bread with which this mixture is charged digest all the same, as well as the gelatinous substances, if the coffee is not used in such quantity as to render them inert . . .

"The use of this mixture is sometimes attended with disagreeable results. Those who are, often eventually have inflammation of the stomach or one of the maladies to which this organ is subject under the abuse thus put upon it. Women especially, from their delicate organization, suffer in the consumption of coffee and milk. To dissuade them from its use it would be well to make them understand that CAFE AU LAIT is nothing in reality but LEATHER SOUP."

Now American and British medical journals are reporting excessive coffee drinking can lead to anxiety, headache, stomach trouble, nervousness, irritability. Writes one: "It is comforting to know that a cup of coffee—minus sugar and cream, of course—need not be a medical no-no." What's "excessive"? Over three cups a day.

The Drug Culture

Cayce was asked numerous questions about the use and affect of various drugs, pills, powders, injections on the market. He almost invariably took a dark view of them, saying that while they may help the particular ailment they would also have long-term, ill effects on the body.

Would sulfa drugs help the strep condition? he was asked. "And make you worse in other conditions? Yes." (*Case #3287-2*) As for the use of bromides, he answered, "(They) *must* eventually become destructive to the physical forces of the body. A hypnotic of any nature continued to be taken must become destructive to the better functioning of the body." (*Case #1264-1*) Again, "any such (headache) powders that act upon the hypogastrics of the system itself as to *deaden* them . . . naturally become detrimental to the body . . ." (*Case #263-1*)

Were hayfever shots in any way responsible for this trouble? someone wanted to know. "Any shots are responsible for almost anything! Yes, they are a part of the disorders." (*Case #3629-1*) Should I discontinue the shots? another man asked of a different drug. "You'd better, if you don't want to get too much of these and cause a heart stroke here!" (*Case #3539-1*) Again, "Are the spinal and liver injections he is getting at times good or harmful?" Answer: "They are not good." (*Case #3580-2*)

What Cayce seems to be saying is that drugs can cure the ailment and kill the patient.

The drug counter has grown even more lethal since Cayce's day. In 1970 it had reached such proportions as to necessitate the Congress passing the Controlled Substances Act containing a long list, that should be longer, of potentially dangerous addictive drugs. Predictably, pharmaceutical manufacturers resist having any of their products so listed. And they all too often win. There's gold in them thar pills.

The process has become a familiar one. A new and dangerous pattern of reaction is belatedly discovered by the government. The Congress threatens to control it. The drug firms, happy with the highly profitable sale, oppose the bill. The Food and Drug Administration, supposedly the regulatory agency and protector of the public, is persuaded to go to Capitol Hill and plead for more time and study of the problem—a convenient dodge. It promises to take appropriate action later. Frequently it is very much later. Meanwhile, the drug is still on the market and casualties mount.

It has happened with amphetamines and barbiturates. More recently it's methaqualone, a sedative-hypnotic often prescribed for insomnia. A few pills make one tipsy; more result in unconsciousness, coma, even death. The public, largely unaware of the possible consequences, continues to buy them.

To put it concisely, the drug that helps you today may do you in tomorrow.

Exercise and the Brain

Fifty years ago Cayce told a 31-year-old man to do his calisthenics. "Well that (the body) should have the regular exercise night and morning. Of morning, the exercise for the upper portion of body. Of evening, before retiring, exercise from the waist down . . . Persistence. Yet with the care and with the attention . . . equalizing circulation; *Remember: In the actions of the physical body the blood forces are carried to the head in the day exercise; and must be equalized over the system by exercise in the evening*, if the body would gain from physical rest that is necessary to keep it in perfect equilibrium. (Italics ours.) Only a few minutes, of course, is necessary, morning and evening, to equalize the circulation and to be ready for the work of the day." (*Case #257–8*)

For some unnamed reason, Cayce stresses that exercise stimulates the circulation of the blood to the head, and that it should be equalized over the entire system as well. He especially recommended stretching, walking, swimming, and head and neck exercises.

Now, Dr. Herbert de Vries and his colleagues at the Gerontology Center of the University of California have been giving simple exercises to retirees that may have far-reaching implications. Three times a week they did calisthenics, stretched, walked, jogged, swam. The volunteers in the experiments reported, as might be expected, that they felt better, enjoyed life more, became more active. But the most notable result as the improvement in "oxygen-transport capacity" the amount of oxygen that the heart delivers to the body.

Earlier research had already shown that brain cells deprived of sufficient oxygen do not perform their work so well, decreasing intellect and reasoning powers that can be damaging. Conversely, mental alertness improves with the supply of pure oxygen which is enhanced by exercise. Senile patients at the Veterans Administration Hospital in Buffalo, New York, when administered pure oxygen for fifteen days, increased their scoring on standard memory tests by as much as twenty-five percent.

Dr. Frederick Jung, American Medical Association consultant, believes inactivity can actually do harm. "Nobody recommends exercise as a cure-all for poor circulation in the brain," he says, "but exercise, in the broadest sense of physical activity, *is* essential for our mental health, especially in the acquisition of new skills, in cooperative adventures with other people, and in competition."

It is known that the brain usually starts to deteriorate with the approach of middle age; and the ability to recognize numbers in a test sequence begins to decline as early as age 27.

To sum up, does exercise make us smarter, more alert? The answer seems to be that it does. Jogging around the block will not only clean out your lungs, it will also clear your brain.

On Baldness

In 1944, a worried, 26-year-old man wrote Edgar Cayce: "Is there any chance of restoring my hair? I am the only one of six brothers who is going bald . . ."

Answer: "Yes. As we find, there is a lack of activity

of the glands in the thyroid areas. This causes a weakness in the activities to nails and hair over the body.

"We would take small doses of Atomidine to purify the thyroid activity. Take one drop each morning for five days in succession. Then leave off for five days. During that period give the scalp a thorough massage with crude oil, using the electrically driven vibrator with the suction applicator. This should be done very thoroughly, not hurriedly, and should require at least thirty to forty minutes for the massage with the crude oil and then the application of white vaseline and then the electrically driven vibrator using the suction cup applicator.

"Then begin the first of the next week with the Atomidine, one drop each morning for five days. Then during the next five days . . . give another crude oil shampoo following with the white vaseline and the vibrator treatment. Leave these off then for two weeks. Then have another complete series, but between each two series allow two weeks to elapse.

"Doing these, we will find that in six to eight months it will begin to stimulate the activities for the growth of hair over the scalp and on body. Do use the diet that carry iodine in their natural forms. Use only kelp salt or deep sea salt. Plenty of sea foods. These are preferable for the body. Not too much sweets. The egg yolk but not the white of egg should be taken. Doing these we will bring better conditions for the body." (*Case #4056-1*)

We do not know the result of this man's experiment, but in 1973 Dr. C. Wilford Grover reported in a survey of those using the treatment the following statistics: 4 percent reported a complete cure; 7 percent considerable hair regrowth; 18 percent a moderate amount of progress. The rest indicated little or no progress. The data also lead to the conclusion that in 84 percent of the cases crude oil prevented further loss of hair and that the probability of considerable or complete hair restoration is increased with treatment for at least twelve months.

On Psychology and
Parapsychology

As the faint scent of change continues drifting in new directions, humanistic psychology and psychoanalysis are adding the sense that man can become more forceful in shaping his life. Whereas Freud tended to undercut the will of man, Italian psychoanalyst Roberto Assagioli believes "The will can be truly called the unknown and neglected factor in modern psychology, psychotherapy, and education." Psychoanalyst Allen Wheelis of San Francisco agrees. Viktor Frankl of Vienna maintains a man's "will to meaning" is more basic than Freud's "will to pleasure". The search to find one's self, to be purposeful, is surely as strong, if not stronger, than the search to enjoy one's self, which for lack of challenge quickly becomes boring.

Assagioli's theory postulates several levels of man's "inner constitution", including a higher realm that is the psychic home of his spiritual, philosophical, and artistic "imperatives". "We walk to the door of religion, but we let the individual open it."

But of all the great psychologists, Carl Jung's most nearly parallels the work of Edgar Cayce. He was the first to recognize the psychic-soul complex, introducing the terms introversion and extroversion. He regarded basic psychic functions to be thinking, feeling, sensation, intuition. He divided the psyche into three phases, as did Cayce, namely: the conscious, unconscious, and

collective unconscious, and between them is a comple-
mentary and compensatory relationship. Cayce called
them the conscious, subconscious, and superconscious.
The collective unconscious he called the Akashic
records. Jung was instrumental in breaking out of the
clutches of superstition the value and meaning of
dreams; Cayce emphasized the importance of their
study. Although they were contemporaries and Cayce
used different terminology, it is unlikely that with his
eighth grade education and preoccupation with religion
he knew anything of the Swiss psychologist.

Jung, like Cayce, was attacked for being unscientific
and mystical, for what he called "the frontier of the
human mind", moving closer and closer to "the port-
cullis of God". He attempted to put his spiritual inclinations into some kind of perspective, and tried to
separate what was scientific in his work from what was
metaphysical.

For this too Jung was attacked. In a letter to a critical
theologian, he once wrote: "You accuse me of repudiat-
ing the divine transcendence altogether. This is not quite
correct. I merely omit it, since I am unable to prove it. I
don't preach; I try to establish psychological facts. I can
confirm and prove the interrelation of the God-image
with other parts of the psyche, but I cannot go further
without committing the error of metaphysical assertion,
which is far beyond my scope."

Deep, honest, unpretentious, he once wrote, "As a
doctor, I am interested in only one thing: how can the
wound be healed?" His greatest asset was that he was
not wedded to prevailing ideas. Jung was a true pioneer.
In his later years, after breaking with Freud, his interests turned to the *I Ching*, to telepathy, Yoga, and
Zen.

The Will and the Mind

The will of man is always supreme, said Cayce, and
he made a distinction between will and mind. "For will
is that with which each soul makes or loses the
opportunities which are its birthright in each exper-

ience . . . The will's influence is always a governing factor, and it may alter the destiny builded by a soul's previous activities.'' (*Case #1770–2*)

Modern, orthodox, scientific tenets recognize neither the soul nor the spirit in man, and downgrade the will and the mind. Instead, it emphasizes the machinations of the brain. Cayce takes a much different view.

"These conditions, mind of the soul, mind of the physical body, mind of the spiritual entity, are separated that one may gain the knowledge of (their) action . . . in the mind of the spiritual entity (we have) that mind wherein the entity . . . manifests in the spiritual plane; the mind in the physical body (is) the subconscious, the conscious, through which the entity manifests in the physical world . . .'' (*Case #900–21*)

In the same discourse he elaborated on the mystical "superconscious". "The superconscious is the divide, that oneness lying between the soul and the spirit force, within the spiritual entity. Not of earth forces at all; only awakened with the spiritual indwelling and acquired individually. It comes to the fore after death, when the conscious mind is dropped and replaced by the subconscious or unconscious.

Cayce's explanations make a certain amount of sense; nevertheless, there is no way of substantiating them.

Dreams and the Unconscious

The unconscious mind plays a greater role in our lives than we might think. Cayce explained it this way: "The dreams, as we see, come to individuals, through the subjugation of the conscious mind (during sleep), and the subconscious being of the soul—when loosed—is able to communicate with the subconscious minds of (other beings) whether in the material or the cosmic plane.'' (*Case #243–5*)

At first glance this may appear to border on the fanciful, but recent cases tend to verify Cayce's contention. The last American soldier to die in the Vietnam War was Lt. Col. William B. Nolde—just eleven hours before the truce was signed. When informed of this at her home in

Mount Pleasant, Michigan, his wife replied, "I knew he wasn't coming back. I knew it the other night. I had a dream. A rocket came in. He said, 'Don't worry, honey, I'm all right.' Then he turned and there was an explosion."

Joyce Nolde told their five children to be prepared because she had a feeling "Dad's gone". On the day the truce was signed in Paris, Colonel Nolde was killed at An Loc by an artillery shell.

Said Cayce: "For as has been given, often there is presented to every normal body with a developing mind those conditions through the subconscious forces of the sleeping state wherein truths are given, visions are seen of things to be warned of and taken advantage of . . . physically, mentally, morally, spiritually, and financially." (*Case #294–34*)

The case of Albert and Theresa Runyan demonstrates that some kind of spiritual communication exists between persons, especially those who have a close relationship.

When Lt. Col. Runyan went to Indochina, he left his wife and four children safely in Sumpter, S.C. But within a few months he was captured and became a prisoner of war. Soon afterwards, he began having dreams about living in Albuquerque, New Mexico.

Back in Sumpter, Theresa Runyan had a sudden inspiration strike her right out of nowhere and for no apparent reason. "One morning I decided we should move to Albuquerque," she recalled. "That was on a Thursday, and by Monday I was here looking at houses. But I never know why I picked Albuquerque until we talked to Al," after his repatriation several years later. "I feel that is why I moved here—because of his dream. He feels I received his dream because he has never been here. I had never been here, either, until I came to look for a house."

Harold Michaels, the administrator of Alameda Hospital in California, had a dream of an airplane disaster in a populated area. He took it seriously and established an elaborate disaster drill program to prepare his staff for such a tragedy. Six months later, a Navy plane crashed into an apartment house. Results: 10 deaths and 41 injuries. But Alameda Hospital's staff was ready. "We could have handled 100 injured, maybe more," said Michaels. "It was incredible," added Dr. Leonard Charvet, chief of the hospital's medical staff.

One of the most pointed cases of the existence of some kind of etheral communication is that of Mrs. Sherman Laughlin. Her son, Tom, was stationed in Vietnam, and she first learned that something had happened to him in an uncommon way.

Very early one morning, she was awakened by what sounded like his voice calling to her. She immediately got up, reached for a piece of scrap paper, and scribbled down her impressions. It is dated February 5, 1968.

"You may think I am crazy," she wrote, "but I was awakened real early this morning and I have a feeling something has happened to Tom. Don't ask me what. I don't know. I woke up weak and sick all over just like he was calling for me and I couldn't get to him."

A few days later, Mrs. Laughlin was officially notified of her son's death on February 5, at a Vietnam time that coincided with the time she was awakened.

Alas, one man's marvel is another man's coincidence.

In March of 1929, Morton Blumenthal, Cayce's financial backer in the construction of the Cayce Hospital, sent the following urgent message: "Dreamed we should sell all our stocks, including box stock (one considered very good). I saw a bull following my wife who was dressed in red." He asked for interpretation.

Cayce went to sleep and said, in essence: "(This is) the impressions of conditions as would come about . . . a downward movement of long duration . . . not allowing, then, those that apparently even are very safe too much latitude . . . Dispose of all held, even those in box; signifies the great amount of change as would come." (*Case #137–115*)

On April 6, Blumenthal submitted another dream: A young chap was blaming him for the murder of a man. A gangster asked, "Is there anyone else in the world who knows this?" He answered, "Miss Cornell. Saw dead man." The gangster started to administer poisonous hypodermic which had been used on the dead man. He felt needle and expected death. Awoke and then went back to sleep. Dreamed interpretation: This represented fight going on in Reserve Board—stock stimulation.

On the same day Cayce gave his reading. "There must surely come a break where there will be panic in the money centers, not only of Wall Street's activity, but a closing of the boards in many other centers and a readjustment of the actual specie . . . high and low quotations to continue for several moons while adjustments are being made." (*Case #137–117*)

On the infamous day of October 29, 1929, the market broke when sixteen million shares changed hands. By the end of the year, stock losses were estimated at fifteen billion dollars, affecting twenty-five million persons.

The intuitive force in man, said Cayce, is universal; we all have it and use it in varying degrees, often unconsciously. "Every entity has clairvoyant, mystic, psychic powers," he asserted, and he advanced the idea many times. The more each is impelled by that which is intuitive, or the relying upon the soul force within, the greater, the farther, the deeper, the broader, the more constructive the result, he claimed.

Even in the conservative, hard-nosed business world, the "hunch" is a prime mover in financial affairs, says E. Douglas Dean, who teaches computer science and statistics at Neward Engineering College. He has tested his theories in a laboratory on more than 100 executives and details his experiments and conclusions in a book, *Executive ESP*, published by Prentice Hall.

In tests, businessmen who had doubled their profits in the past five years vie with unsuccessful executives in an elaborate guessing game. In one, a computer threw out numbers at random an hour after the men predicted what the numbers would be. The big money-makers beat the also-rans every time.

Dean believes that solid business experience can be gained. "With ESP," he conjectured, "you either have it or you don't." A past-president of the Parapsychological Association, Dean thinks ESP ability matches up with executives' experience in making decisions on "gut feelings in flat contradiction of known facts".

The Securities and Exchange Commission is showing uneasy interest in ESP on Wall Street. An investment advisor has run ads stating that a "new approach to stock market forecasting combines a specific ESP factor with traditional fundamental and technical methods". The SEC doesn't like it.

Orthodox science has long argued that psychic phenomena are not matters of scientific interest and that there is no proof that they exist. Yet new evidence, although not conclusive, continues to come to light.

Two physicists from the Stanford Research Institute, a private "Think Tank" with 3600 highly trained specialists, reported in 1973 that they had examined the psychic powers of Uri Geller, the Israeli night club performer. After six weeks of tests, they found he could perform numerous feats for which they had no explanation, one of which was bending metal objects.

Under controlled laboratory conditions, one of a pair of ordinary dice was placed in a metal box and shaken. Young Geller envisioned the face figures of the dice ten times; he was correct eight times and passed twice. In another test, an object was shown to Geller and then hidden in one of ten aluminum cans. He was asked to pick the can by first naming all the empty ones. He did this twelve times without error, a one-in-a-trillion chance, although twice he declined to name the can. Simple pictures of airplanes, houses, and symmetrical objects were drawn on file cards while Geller was away from the Institute, sealed in envelopes and locked in a safe. When shown the opaque envelopes, Geller drew seven exact reproductions without error. The Stanford group concluded that "further investigation is clearly warranted", and that psychic phenomena is "a legitimate subject for scientific inquiry". Geller has moved the hands of clocks, bent a stream of flowing water, cooked raw eggs, repaired broken watches without touching them.

No matter. When *Time* magazine and Department of Defense officials were invited to observe Geller in action, they were, as might be expected, unconvinced. Deception and trickery were surely involved, matters in which they are experts. *Time*, of course, lost no time in giving Geller a bad press, claiming his feats were all tricks that any good trickster could perform.

One can only hope that further tests on Uri Geller by Cambridge University professors will either confirm or deny his psychic abilities. Significantly, he reportedly doesn't like to perform before magicians.

On Meditation

Fifty years ago, Cayce was urging people to "meditate in the law of the Lord", and he didn't mean just to think about it. "It is not musing, not daydreaming; but as ye find your bodies made up of the physical, mental and spiritual, it is the attuning of the mental body and the physical body to (their) spiritual source." He associates meditation with the endocrine glands of the body and their purification.

"But there are physical contacts which the anatomist finds not, or those who would look for imaginations of the mind. Yet it is found that within the body there are channels, there are ducts, there are glands, there are activities that perform no-one-knows-what in a living, *moving*, thinking being. In many individuals, such become dormant. Many have atrophied. Why? Nonusage, non-activity! . . . because only the desires of the appetites, self-indulgences and such, have so glossed over or used up the abilities in these directions that they become only wastes, as it were, in the spiritual life of an individual who has so abused or misused those abilities that have been given him for the greater activity." (*Case #281-41*)

In prayer, we speak to God; in meditation, God

speaks to us if we only listen to that still small voice within, he said. "With the periods set aside for meditation—don't hurry yourself, don't be anxious, but closing the self, the conscious mind to anxieties from without—enter within thine own inner temple. There let the voice, the feeling direct; yea, let the spirit of the purpose of self be free in its direction to self. Attune yourself almost in the same manner as you tune the violin for harmony. For when the body-mind and the soul-mind is attuned to the infinite, there will be brought harmony to the mind, and those centers from which impulse arises will aid in the directing of the individual entity to become more sensitive, and the material things about the entity may be the better enjoyed." (*Case #1861–18*)

Meditation is now becoming popular, not only with the occultists and the Bible Hippies, but in the orthodox churches. Even so conventional a publication as *Reader's Digest* ran an article entitled "The Art of Meditation". The art, of course, as the *Digest* points out, has been around for millenia. "Meditation," said Aldous Huxley, "has been used in every part of the world and from the remotest periods as a method for acquiring knowledge about the essential nature of things."

The youth of today take a similar view. Said one: "It's the greatest adventure of them all. You don't know what you're going to find, but whatever it is, you know it's going to change your life."

The requirements for meditation are a quiet place, a still mind emptied of all worldly thoughts, an attitude of receptive openness, and, Cayce insisted, concentration on a spiritual affirmation. A straight, comfortable position, sitting or lying without legs or arms crossed, is best, for better circulation. Success may not come in ten minutes or ten days, but meditators claim good results in finding the answers to problems and in self-discovery.

Tests of human response to deep meditation reveal some astonishing results. *Scientific American* magazine reported that breathing, oxygen consumption, and metabolic rate markedly decrease, indicating a state of rest and serenity. Skin resistance increases, whereas in anxiety it decreases. And the concentration of lactate in the blood decreases. High concentration of lactate has been associated with anxiety and high blood pressure.

Other research shows that cardiac output goes down, reducing the work-load of the heart. Conversely, mental reaction time and alertness improve, along with better hearing, suggesting greater perception and sensitivity.

The University of Cologne's Freiburger Personality Inventory test revealed that the practice of meditation reduced nervousness, aggression, depression, irritability; and increased sociability, self-confidence, cordiality, efficiency, and staying power. Harvard and the University of California have also done research experiments with favorable results. Other reliable laboratory tests dispute mystical meanings: similar results are obtained while in a mere state of repose.

There are pragmatic reasons why interest in meditation has grown in recent years. Studies show that students of meditation have fewer drug problems. The Illinois state legislature, noting that the practice "shows promise of being the most positive and effective drug prevention program being presented in the world today", passed a resolution endorsing transcendental meditation. A board of education coordinator told a congressional committee that he would like to try a meditation program in public schools. Representative Bella Abzug, who doesn't hesitate to call a spade a dirty shovel, endorsed the idea, adding, "As a matter of fact, I think fifteen-minute meditation sessions might be very helpful, particularly to the executive branch of government."

The National Institute of Mental Health is also convinced. It has awarded a grant of $21,000 to train 120 school teachers to teach the "Science of Creative Intelligence" in high schools. Maharishi Mahesh Yogi, the High Inca of Transcendental Meditation, is seeking to create 3600 centers around the world to train teachers in the use of a video-based package developed at his Los Angeles headquarters.

Meditation, it appears, has finally "arrived". Said Cayce: ". . . for the time has arisen in the earth when men everywhere seek to know more of the mysteries of the mind, the soul, the soul's mind which man recognizes as existent." (*Case #254–52*) He places the emphasis on *spiritual* meditation "in the law of the Lord".

The Electro-Spiritual

Whatever electricity is to man, that's what the power of God is, said Cayce. There is no force other than One Force in its various phases. We are and live in a world of electro-spiritual vibrations.

"Each atomic force of a physical body is made up of its units of positive and negative forces that brings it into a *material* plane. These are of the ether, or atomic forces, being electric in nature as they enter into a material basis, or become *matter* in its ability to take on or throw off." (*Case #281–3*)

We are immersed in a natural field of static electricity, science has discovered, and all of us have experienced a shock by simply walking across a rug and touching a metal door knob. The atmosphere of the earth is supplied with a positive charge that causes a downward electric field amounting to between 100 and 500 volts per meter on a clear day. In the out-of-doors at the higher value, there could be 1000 volts bombarding the earth up to a height of six to seven feet.

How does man survive? He is a grounded conductor and actually there is no voltage on him. His body and skin warp the electric field of the atmosphere and he is unaware of the positive charge surrounding him.

Cayce claims that ". . . every form of life that man sees in a material world is an essence or manifestation of the Creator; not the Creator but a manifestation of a first cause . . ." (*Case #5753–1*) He also says there is no time; it is one time. There is no space; it is one space.

We have, of course, no way of objectively proving or disproving such statements.

The Healing Spirit

Is spiritual healing possible? Cayce claims that it is, and more; all healing is spiritual healing. There is a kind of intelligent spirit in each cell of the body, and it is this, he says, that does the healing. Medicines may aid and hasten the process, but the body does its own healing.

Asked about the laying on of hands, he once answered: "This may be developed in self, even as the vibrations may be raised in self and in others. When there is that impelling force that arises to *do* by work *or* by act, or by that rising in self, *act* in *that* direction and manner." (*Case #281–10*)

Again: "As we find here, the relaxings of the body by or through suggestions made as to almost hypnotize the body, will help. This should be done by the power of suggestion at the same time that applications would be made for magnetic healing. This may be done by the very close associates of the body." (*Case #3619–1*)

We know that hypnotism will work in some cases, at least temporarily. So-called "Faith Healers" may even use it on the naive in religious spectaculars. But so far there is little to support most claims of spiritual healings.

A symposium sponsored by Stanford University and the Academy of Parapsychology and Medicine of Los Altos, Calif., indicated that some mysterious form of energy can indeed flow from one person to another. Some people, it is believed, are especially capable of transferring such energy, and thus can serve as healers. A doctor of biochemistry who has researched the laying on of hands, suggested a single energy or force is probably responsible for all parapsychological phenomena. Another had similar evidence of an energy transfer in the laying on of hands.

Dr. Bernard Grad of the Department of Psychiatry, McGill University, Montreal, reported in 1972 that he has demonstrated that there is a healing energy force in the laying on of hands. Using mice with goiters, he subjected them to persons claiming healing powers. The mice so "treated" had a slower growth rate of goiter than the untreated ones. He did not report that any of the mice recovered, however.

A great deal of work needs to be done to validate claims of spiritual healing. But some progress is being made. Dr. Thelma S. Moss, assistant professor of psychiatry at the University of California, is using a photographic method which she believes records an aura of energy in and around all living matter, including plants. Russian scientists have had similar results. Objects of all kinds seem to radiate a form of luminescence —tiny, white bubbles that literally burst with a mysterious form of energy. In spiritual healing—to which the Soviets lay no claim—Dr. Moss says the fingertip aura of the healer is usually smaller, while the aura of the person being healed increases.

It appears that enough has been done to warrant serious inquiry. Many years ago, Cayce said of the aura: "Auras are two-fold: That which indicates the physical emanations and that which indicates the spiritual development . . . the emanation that arises from the very vibratory influences of an individual entity, mentally, spiritually—especially of the spiritual forces." (*Case #319-2*)

Newsweek, which takes a relatively forward looking view of things psychic, quoted psychologist Lawrence Le Shan as saying that "At least 90 percent of all psychic healing cases reported are not genuine, but the other 10 percent are solid cases medically diagnosed as incurable . . . Then suddenly, after a psychic-healing session, the observed symptoms no longer exist."

Spirit Possession

Not all "spiritual forces" are benevolent, however, according to Cayce. He not only claims the departed soul entity goes on to other adventures in the outer realms after death, but that some incorrigible spirits return surreptitiously to the earth to do nothing more than make mischief. On several occasions he confirmed "possession" by disincarnate entities.

"What causes my husband to lose control of himself?" he was asked.

"Possession!"

"What is meant by possession?"

"Means POSSESSION!"

"Is he crazy or mentally deranged?"

"If possession isn't crazy, what is it?"

"Does possession mean by other entities, while under the influence of liquor?"

"By other entities while under the influence of liquor. For this body, if there could be a sufficient period of refraining from the use of alcoholic stimulants and the diathermy electrical treatments used, such treatments would drive these entities out! But do not use electrical treatments with the effects of alcohol in the system, it would be detrimental!" (*Case #1183-3*)

To an altogether different type person, he said: "The body is a supersensitive individual entity who has allowed itself—through study, through opening the gland centers of the body—to become possessed with activities outside of itself . . ."

"How did I pick this up?" the 53-year-old woman asked.

"The body, in its study, opened the gland centers and allowed self to become sensitive to outside influences."

"What is it exactly that assails me?"

"Outside influences. Disincarnate entities." (*Case #5221-1*)

To another, a 39-year-old woman, he reiterated the importance of the glands. "There has been the opening of the lyden (Leydig) gland, so that the kundaline forces move along the spine to the various centers that open— with the activities of the mental and spiritual forces of the body . . . The psychological reaction is much like that which may be illustrated in one gaining much (spiritual) knowledge without making practical application of it . . . Now combine these two and we have that indicated here as a possession of the body—a gnawing, as it were, on all of the seven (endocrine) centers of the body, causing the inability to rest or even a concerted activity—unless the body finds itself needed for someone else. Then the body finds, as this occurs, the disturbance is retarded or fades as the body exercises itself in giving help to others." (*Case #3421-1*)

Possession manifests in numerous ways, often in children, by changes in personality, thrown objects, upset furniture, inexplicable noises. A New Jersey case made the headlines for several days and the strange, forceful movement of household items was never otherwise satisfactorily explained.

In San Francisco in the summer of 1973, a team of Roman Catholic priests performed the rites of exorcism to liberate a family of demonic possession. The two-year-old son of the young couple appeared to be the focal point, although all three suffered physical manifestations of being choked and their belongings hurled across a room, one a knife that imbedded in a wall. The priests and a physician testified that the choking attacks left visible bruises.

"But," said the Reverend Miles O'Brien Riley, Director of the San Francisco Archdiocese Communications Center, "this story has a happy ending. And what makes it all the better is that it is not fiction, that it is all true." The unnamed family "went through the experience, and it worked out," he said, after the priests prayed for fifteen days and nights for the family's deliverance.

Predictably, a disbelieving psychoanalyst made the news with a dubious put-down by declaring the whole thing traceable to "childhood experiences".

The Archbishop of Canterbury, Michael Ramsey, declared that there are genuine demonic powers in the world, but that many claimed cases of possession "by the devil" are mostly "a lot of fiddlesticks". "There are forces of evil of a supernatural kind that sometimes get hold of people," he said. "There are genuine exorcisms.

But there is also a lot of phony superstition around . . .
it's a very dangerous gift to use. There is the danger of
the person using it being spiritually damaged. I would
not advise it for anybody if he didn't have the gift and
considerable spiritual depth.''

In this, Cayce concurs.

Law and Morality

Among the earth's most spiritual-minded peoples—
and there are a number of them—are none other than
the native Americans. Cayce made the claim many
years ago when he said: "For the peoples (North
American Indians) then understood—even better than
they do today—how that the heavens declare the glory
of God, and as to how nature *sings* His praises in the
rebirth at each period, each cycle, for its unfoldment
and growth . . ." (*Case #2438–1*)

"The entity then was among the (Indian) princesses
of the land that established there the teachings of the
Law of *One* (One religion, One state, One mate, One
home, One God) . . . Then the entity established what
may be called the home life in that land, as each home
became then as the castle or place of worship . . ." (*Case
#851–2*)

The genius of North American Indian tribes was that
they were able to govern themselves without any re-
course to criminal codes, written rules, or regulations.
"Crime and offenses were so infrequent under (the
Iroquios) system," wrote lawyer and anthropologist
Lewis Henry Morgan in 1847, "that (they) can scarcely
be said to have had a criminal code."

The Indians developed a rule of custom in which
religion, politics, and economics merged into one viable
tradition as a way of life. Living communally, there
were no rich and no poor. "The primary virtue," writes
lawyer-historian Vine Deloria, Jr., a Sioux, "was an individual's integrity. If a person was not as good as his
word, then the whole society was injured. People had to
be able to count on each other since no authority existed

to enforce rules, and no one really *had* to do anything unless it became a point of personal honor. Honor alone was likely to insure calm social conditions within a tribe."

If a tribe or village could not remain together on the basis of mutual respect and trust, it simply disintegrated as a collective society. American Indians believed, and many still do, that the purpose of social existence is to develop the human being. Sadly enough, when the white man arrived he took this as a sign of weakness.

In the Hopi religion, which is inseparable from their daily lives, all things including the earth are alive, and the people felt charged with the responsibility of protecting life and nature. Pacific in character, they were opposed to war and were honest and industrious, reported the first U.S. Indian Agent to the Southwest in 1849.

To this day, the Hopis and Navajos shun the white man's competitiveness and pursuit of power and wealth. According to their religion, the earth has been destroyed three times because of greed and war. Each time *Massau'u*, the Great Spirit, gave man another chance and each time he failed. Now we are living in the fourth world, and it may be the last. "The prophecy says there will be paths in the sky," writes John Lansa. "The paths are airplanes. There will be cobwebs in the air. These are the power lines. Great ashes will be dumped on cities and there will be destruction. These are the atom bombs America dropped on Hiroshima. The prophecy says men will travel to the moon and stars and this will cause disruption. It is bad that spacemen brought things back from the moon. That is very bad."

"Selfishness is the greater fault in *most* individuals," the Virginia Beach seer said more than once. "There should be set before self an ideal, a *spiritual* ideal. Not such an ideal that, 'I would like to have a house like John Smith's, and a wife that dresses like Mrs. Smith, and a car like John Smith's boy runs, or a dog or a horse such as those.' *That's* Material! Rather set an ideal in the *spiritual* sense and know that he that would be greatest among men will be the servant of all." (*Case #912-1*)

Servants are considered at the bottom of the pecking order, and the lower the order the lower the servant. Yet history shows that truly great individuals were indeed the servants of the many, often at no little sacrifice to themselves. Their names are legion, and they are the ones who have led the way to higher ground.

A person all wrapped up in himself makes a pretty small package. For all have only one basic sin: *Self*. From it, Cayce insisted, flows all others. Love is giving, and the greatest of all virtues is service to others. "The purpose in life, then," he told more than one inquirer, "is not the gratifying of appetites nor of any selfish desires, but it is that the entity, the soul, may make the earth, where the entity finds its consciousness, a better place in which to live . . . You have a greater opportunity at the present time than you will have at any other period of this particular sojourn, *so* you'd better be up and doing, keeping self in accord with God's laws." (*Case #4047-2*)

He spelled it out this way: "To do good, to eschew evil, to love mercy and judgment, saith the prophet, is the whole duty of man—as related to his activities in the earth. And what saith the Son, the Christ? 'To love the Lord with all thy heart, thy mind, thy body, and thy neighbor as thyself.' This is the whole will of the Father to His children. The rest of that recorded in Holy Writ—as may be said by man in his relationships, in meeting the problems of every day, every experience—is merely the attempt to explain, to analyze, to justify or to meet that saying, that truth; which must, which will become a consciousness, an awareness in the experience of those who seek to do His will in the earth.

"What is His will? That ye love one another, and ACT in that manner." (*Case #2524-3*)

Christianity puts it this way: "All things whatsoever that ye would that men should do to you, do ye so to them; for this is the law and the prophets."

Judaism says: "What is hateful to you, do not to your fellow man; that is the entire law; all the rest is commentary."

Buddhism explains it as: "Hurt not others in ways that yourself would find hurtful."

Zoroastranism teaches: "That nature alone is good which refrains from doing unto others whatsoever is not good for itself."

Islam says: "No one of you is a believer until he desires for his brother that which he desires for himself."

Brahmanism puts it as: "This is the sum duty: Do not unto others that which would cause you pain if done to you."

Confucianism asks: "Is there one maxim which ought to be acted upon throughout one's whole life?" And answers: "Surely it is the maxim of loving kindness: Do not unto others what you would not have them do unto you."

And Taoism states it thusly: "Regard your neighbor's gain as your gain, and your neighbor's loss as your loss."

The Cayce records seem to sum it all up with these words: "So we have LOVE IS LAW, LAW IS LOVE, GOD IS LOVE, LOVE IS GOD. In that we see the law manifested, not the law itself . . . the individual . . . that gets the understanding of self becomes a part of this . . . if we as individuals, upon the earth plane, have all of the other elementary forces that make to the bettering of life, and have not love, we are as nothing—*nothing*." (*Case #3744–4*)

More succinctly: ". . . not then, in the amount of moneys, lands, holdings, houses, cattle nor gold, but in that ability to *serve thine brother* lies strength, security, and the perfect knowledge of God." (*Case #900–370*)

On Man and the Universe

What is there about man and the earth that make them so distinctive? Nothing in the known universe closely resembles either. Obviously, it is more than man's comparative anatomy, physiology, or neurology that sets him apart. Of the planets, only Earth is suited to meet his needs.

From the Greek philosophers down to the present, there have been men who said that man is more than matter; that he has a kind of soul or spirit or self-consciousness that is supreme in the earth, and that something so intangible and electric may survive death. The primary question has to do with the reality of the mind and whether it is a non-physical element. A similar problem is the spiritual or non-spiritual basis of the human personality. Psychology and parapsychology are studying these enigmas, but Edgar Cayce's answers are clearly in the affirmative.

Science has taken the miraculous out of the supernatural and converted it to the natural and the superphysical. Yet to declare something as "natural" does not sufficiently explain it; we need to know why and what makes it "natural". Because we can partially explain and understand a phenomenon does not make it less marvelous. We don't even know what life is, although we know a great deal about it. And we know even less about death.

Cayce claims that the universe came into being through Mind, the mind of the Maker, the vibration of positive and negative forces, and that worlds are still being created by the same process. That we have an expanding universe is now widely accepted. Scientific evidence has not confirmed the first claim, but it appears to be working in that direction.

Said Cayce: "The mind of God embraces the one total life energy with its universally evolved portion called mind, in all of its forms, all its stages of development, and all of its self-conscious, individual viewpoints, including ourselves." (*Case #792-Ca*) God is Time, Space, and Patience, and all time is one. The First Cause, the Universal Force, was "God", and the creation and preparation for future needs "has gone down many, many thousands and millions of years" to provide "for the needs of man in the hundreds and thousands of years to come." (*Case #3744-4* in 1923)

There is no way of proving or disproving all this, but some of our modern concepts of a purely mechanical, materialistic, accidental world have been rudely challenged. When Einstein defined the electron as a "field of force" and a "sphere of influence", not a speck of matter, he upset the accepted scheme of things.

Are worlds still being created as Cayce claimed? It may be so. In 1969-70, researcher Joseph Weber of the University of Maryland startled the scientific world with his detection of pulses of gravitational radiation coming from outer space. The discovery implied the occurrence of cataclysmic events in the center of the galaxy. Weber's experiment has not been duplicated by others, such as attempts by J. A. Tyson of Bell Laboratories, suggesting that the radiation may be variable and currently not emitting. At least fourteen other research individuals and groups are working on the problem of gravitational impulses from space, and Weber's findings may yet be confirmed.

The atom, the basis of matter, has turned out to be not matter, but energy. The impact of a force field called "thought" on photographic emulsion, the power of thought-processes affecting cell growth in plants, psychosomatic medicine, and extrasensory perception indicate the unseen is more powerful than the seen. The most potent of all man's tools is the idea.

That the universe is made up of positive and negative charges, as Cayce claimed, is demonstrated in the discovery of electricity, atoms, and antimatter. Antimatter was first theorized by Paul Dirac, a British physicist, in 1928. Scholars have since confirmed its reality in cosmic rays and atom smashers. In 1973, Russian scientists of the Institute of High Energy Physics and the Joint Institute of Nuclear Research reported new evidence. By using their biggest atom smasher, they say they have created and detected antimatter, the counterpart of tritium, a heavy radioactive isotope of hydrogen.

Antimatter is the counterpart of ordinary matter—antiprotons instead of protons, positrons instead of electrons, antineutrons instead of neutrons. The proton is a positive charge, the electron negative, the neutron neutral. The hypothesis is that the universe is made up symmetrically of ordinary matter and antimatter and that the mutual annihilation of both may produce a new form of valuable energy. Enormous regions of the universe contain clusters of galaxies, one consisting of matter and the other of antimatter, along with adjacent matter/antimatter fields.

Dr. Behram Kursunoglu, a University of Miami physicist, has come up with a theory that challenges existing scientific belief. He contends that the universe is a smoldering inferno originally ignited by two microblack holes of antimatter. He says he has developed and mathematically explained history's third major theory of the birth and evolution of the universe.

"I am supremely confident that the theory will hold up, otherwise, I would not talk so freely," he declared in December of 1973. He is convinced that ten billion years ago there was no matter, only an eerie, omnipresent field of energy. Then, some supernatural force upset the field by manufacturing two microscopic elementary particles. Although miniscule, the particles were held together by a tremendous energy. The two microblack holes or particles triggered massive fires throughout the field. A gigantic chain reaction fabricated more and more particles which darted around until they clustered together in various forms and locations. Kursunoglu believes they were the building blocks of the gasses, stars, planets, and eventually life itself.

Antimatter, which may be described as a mirror-like image of matter, has been produced in laboratories but has not been observed in its natural state. Kursunoglu plans to present his mathematical equations to the American Physical Society.

"Today there is a wide measure of agreement," says British physicist and astronomer, Sir James Jeans, "which on the physical side of science approaches almost to unanimity, that the stream of knowledge is heading toward a non-mechanical reality; the universe begins to look more like a great thought than like a great machine. Mind no longer appears as an accidental intruder into the realm of matter. We are beginning to suspect that we ought rather to hail it as the creator and governor of the realm of matter."

The old logic has been shaken: Break up matter into its ultimate constituents; discover its properties; duplicate them—and presto, you will have the secret of matter. Dr. Raynor C. Johnson, the Australian physicist, and a few other scientists have boldly declared that the creation and maintenance of the universe rests upon "universal Mind".

We may indeed live in a world consisting of vibrations and the "relativity of force", as the sleeping prophet indicated a half century ago. The material is not as solid as we think, for wood burns and steel melts. Do we inhabit a world not of matter but of condensed energy of varying rates of fluidity, including ourselves?

The Advent of Man

In man's search for the underlying cause and source

of energy, he has generally looked everywhere but inside himself. Yet there is historic as well as current and growing evidence that energy is also a property of us and within us, and can be applied externally in the fall of dice and the telepathic movement of objects.

Dr. Shafica Karagulla, an American M.D. and a distinguished psychiatrist now researching in the psychic, has said: "You begin to get a picture of man not only as a dense physical form, but man made up of several types of energies, and that the solid form is the by-product—the final condensation—rather than the primary factor."

Dr. Karagulla is studying the mental, psychic, physical, cosmic forces of man and how they can be integrated into the field of medicine. "This (cosmic) energy field is the vital field around every atom, every molecule, the planets, the solar system, the galaxies," she asserts. "It is believed (by the ancients) that the human being takes an aspect of it and condenses it within his form and makes that part which is himself." The etheric field is thus the ultimate source of energy. "It is all around us and we take that which we need, we create our form, our pattern of energy, of what we are and then we give it out . . ."

Man has generated electricity, harnessed steam, split the atom, but he still doesn't know where the energy comes from.

The popular, fashionable conception of man is deterministic, materialistic, mechanistic, naturalistic. It holds that man is solely the product of the natural or physical world, although the meaning of the word "natural" and its implications of universal law, order and harmony are never quite explained. Mental or psychological events are not causes, but, like behavior, simply effects. We are controlled and shaped entirely by heredity and environment, the former being also a result of environment.

The argument is as full of holes as a mosquito net. The individuality, the personality, the will, the talents, the idiosyncracies of human beings—their likes and dislikes, loves and hates, vices and virtues—are still largely unaccounted for. Twins, we know, often have widely varying personalities although reared in similar environment. Genes and heredity—which appear to be overdrawn—explain how, not why.

The atheistic view, as the religious view, is based on faith, intuition, and aesthetic experience, not on empirical evidence. Purely empirical evidence cannot prove or disprove either Humanism or theism. The discussion is almost but not quite reduced to a philosophical one.

Man has great capacities that give him extraordinary control over himself and his destiny. Yet with all his knowledge of the world in which he lives, he still knows almost nothing of the forces that make him human. He only knows he is different, distinctive, and superior to the plant and animal kingdoms. Endowed with free will and reason, he can choose the path he will follow to express his creative instincts. He is also the only animal that laughs, cries, and tells lies.

The Cayce records have a great deal to say about man and the human soul. They generally corroborate the Mosaic story of creation in principle if not in detail. All souls were created in the beginning and are working their way back whence they came. Adam and Eve with their contemporaries—"the fall of the angels"—were special creations, not the result of happenstance. Man is not a cosmic orphan.

"The soul of each entity is as a corpuscle in the body of God," said Cayce. "The soul is that which the Maker gave to every entity or individual in the beginning." And again, "Spirit is the life, mind is the builder, the physical is the result." "Man was made as man," he said. "There (were), there (are), as we find only three of the creations . . . matter, force, and mind . . . All flesh is not of one flesh, but the developing of one has always remained in the same (form), and has only been to meet the needs of man, for which there was made all that was made, and man's evolving or evolution has only been . . . the gradual growth upward to the mind of the Maker." (*Case #3744-4*)

"The first cause was that the created would be the companion for the Creator; that it, the creature, would—through its manifestations in the activities of that given unto the creature—show itself to be not only worthy of, but companionable to the Creator." (*Case #5753-1*) It is man's free will and reason—the manifestations of the soul—that sets him apart from the animal kingdom, Cayce insists. Will is that power given to each soul at the time of creation which enables it to choose its direction of activity. "There is set before thee good and evil; choose thou," he said. "This was true in the beginning; it is true today." Man, it seems, is a speck of the divine wrapped in a ball of ego climbing a slippery slope.

The will of man is supreme. Heredity and environment, reincarnation and karma, play their parts in influencing, he said, but the will through the mind makes the decisions, often against all logic. "Then a soul, the offspring of a Creator, entering into a consciousness that became a manifestation in any plane or sphere of activity, given that free will for its use of those abilities, qualities, conditions in its experience, demonstrates, manifests, shows forth that it reflects in its activity towards that first cause." (*Case #5753-1*)

Few scientists would concur in all this, and fewer still are willing to buck the current rationale of "operant conditioning", i.e., rewarding desired responses; that will-less man can be altered by conditioning. The trouble is that some brains can't be brainwashed.

With the advent of psychology, the soul was "out" and the brain was "in", although in classical or philosophical psychology, the soul was a central concept. In our over-simplified, rationalized, mechanistic world, psychology is regarded as the "Science of the brain". Yet Carl Jung's precepts relate it to the true psyche—the soul force in man and the "collective unconscious" of the whole. Dr. June Singer, a Jungian, in her recent book, *Boundaries of the Soul*, states that while psychology is a subject that has its scientific aspects, it is essentially beyond the reach of science and the laboratory. She explores both the known and the unknown of the human psyche in support of Jung—and coincidentally, much of what Cayce has to say about the soul. "You would not find out the boundaries of the soul," she quotes Heraclitus, "even by travelling along every path; so deep a measure does it have."

A few other brave "souls" in the scientific world also dispute the current theories. One is that grand old man of science, Sir John Eccles. The Australian scholar-scientist-philosopher believes that man has a free will and a soul that just might be immortal. "I absolutely refuse to say that I am not more than the sum of my parts," he admonishes with good humor. "I believe we are more than that. We are unique beings, conscious of our very selves. I resist completely the idea that all our actions are motivated by inheritance and conditioning alone."

Eccles, winner of the Nobel Prize in 1963 for his contributions to an understanding of the human brain, believes that materialistic, mechanistic psychologists "have done a rotten job in education". He is convinced that to deny free will is not a rational act. All responses are simply not reflexes. In opposition to the teachings of the Skinner school of thought, Eccles adamantly says, "Free will in man is a reality and should not be denied because we can't explain it."

Much to the disgust of many psychologists, various independent thinkers are returning to the concept of the soul. Roberto Assagioli of Florence, Italy, a doctor, psychotherapist and teacher, maintains that science needs to recognize man's highest qualities in order to complement and complete the prevailing emphasis on his instincts, drives, complexes, pathology. The central idea in his *Height Psychology and the Self* is the notion of the Self with a capital "S". The Self and the soul are almost synonymous. "At our higher human level," he says, "there is an entity that is at the center of the higher functions—artistic inspiration, ethical insight, scientific intuition. This is our real core; it is there in all of us, but the personality is generally not aware of it at the ordinary level.''

Speaking of the symbols in the *Book of Revelation*, Cayce once said: ''These we see, then, represent *self*; self's body-physical, self's body-mental, self's body-spiritual; with the attributes of the body-physical, attributes of the body-mental, attributes of the body-spiritual, and they are *one* in thee—even as the Father, the Son, and the Holy Spirit is one in Him.'' (*Case #281-16*)

Jung described his rather complicated concept of the soul as follows: ''With the same justification as daily experience furnishes us for speaking of an outer personality are we also justified in assuming the existence of an inner personality. The inner personality is the manner of one's behavior towards the inner psychic processes; it is the inner attitude, the character, that is turned towards the unconscious. I term the outer attitude . . . the *persona*, the inner attitude I term the *anima*, or soul.''

Science has not been able to prove or disprove the reality of a spirit force, but some of its findings nevertheless tend to support psychic instinct and intuition. Parapsychology has achieved remarkable results, yet it is still not ''respectable'' in the eyes of many. The Department of Defense quietly made grants to investigate the possibility that homing pigeons used ESP and that dogs used it to locate land mines. Favorable results in the experiments were not published until 1971, after remaining classified for twenty years. The National Aeronautics and Space Administration has done some unofficial probing in the use of ESP in space flights, as have the Russians. Government intelligence agencies are also interested, but are wary because of the risk of embarrassing publicity.

Cayce once made a curious comment in which he appeared to be making use of a bit of poetic license. ''In that before this, we find in the beginning, when the first of the elements were given, and the forces set in motion that brought about the sphere as we find called the earth plane. (This was when) the morning stars sang together, and the whispering winds brought the news of the coming of man's indwelling, of the spirit of the Creator, and he, man, became the living soul." (*Case #294-8*)

In the light of recent developments this may be more than poetry. D. Scott Rogo, in his volume, *A Psychic Study of the Music of the Sphere*, maintains that psychic music is for real. The subject is explored extensively in his analyses of fifty-eight first-hand cases in the United States. Of more than one hundred individual cases, half were scrupulously disqualified for one reason or another.

Cosmic music is most often heard subjectively, he claims, when the percipient is about to fall asleep, is deeply engrossed in nature or in contemplation, or is in a state of extreme depression. Others have reported it being heard by observers at the death watch. Percipients declare it as choral or orchestral and "more beautiful and perfect" than any music heard normally. Unlike earthly, man-made melodies, it is often described as like "angels singing". Most said they could neither remember nor reproduce it.

To Rogo, it appears that psychic music is a property of the "next world" and that those who perceive it do so during out-of-the-body experiences or at near death, when they are closer to the next world. "In my interpretation," he writes, "the psychic ether becomes the border between this world and the 'next world'. All psychic phenomena can be explained as working through the psychic ether."

When souls pass over to the other side, claimed Cayce, the entity takes on a spiritual body, not a material one. There is no life of any kind on the other planets, he asserted: In the context of the readings, perhaps only human life within the solar system. ". . . only upon the earth plane at present do we find man is flesh and blood, but upon others do we find those of his own making in the preparation of his own development." *(Case #3744-3)*

Those statements weren't too unbelievable when he made them, but they are highly questionable by some today. Many scientists not only believe that physical life on other planets is possible, but that communication is feasible. In 1968, a team of astronomers and physicists at the University of California discovered evidence of water and ammonia in interstellar space. The two are vital to life and the revelation raises new hope that life of some kind may be found within the next ten years. They're still looking.

The degree of scholarly seriousness was shown in 1971, when the first international conference on the problem was held in the Soviet Union. Jointly sponsored by the American and Russian academies of science, the meeting was attended by experts in the fields of astronomy, biology, physics, chemistry, computer science, linguistics, anthropology, and other disciplines. They agreed that contact with extraterrestrial life was likely enough to justify starting a variety of search programs, and the present technology was sufficient for the job.

In 1972, Professor Richard Berendzen of NASA and Boston University's astronomy department, organized a symposium to discuss the significance of the conference. Entitled "Life Beyond Earth and the Mind of Man", it drew an overflow audience of scholars. By 1973, Soviet researchers thought they had picked up signals from outer space. American scientists disagreed, saying the signals were from secret spy satellites orbiting the earth.

Cayce may yet prove to be wrong, although the non-evidence so far is hardly persuasive either way. Astronaut James Irwin, a member of the Apollo-15 mission, is inclined toward the Cayce view. "The earth, in my opinion, occupies a sole position in the group of planets that make up our solar system. On the moon, we all know now that life does not exist. I, who had the honor to step on the moon surface and could see the earth at an entirely different angle, felt a great peace when I was there. I felt God's presence." UFO's could still be real—from beyond the solar system.

Evolution vs Creationism

Modern hostility toward a divine creation is due, in part, to a scientific prejudice arising from non-scientific assumption; that there can be no spiritual intervention in the workings of the universe: the scientific method is the only route to truth.

There are, of course, other approaches to truth. "The creationist model may not be scientific," writes one physical scientist, "but I cannot believe that many of the models presented by biologists of the origin of and the evolution of species are less speculative. It is in the highest tradition of science to allow opposing viewpoints to be heard rather than insisting that only one side be taught in a school text book."

Objections are raised to creationism being taught in schools because it is a "theory of primordial history". But evolutionism is also a theory of primordial history as it is used to explain the origin of species. Any theory of origins is, in fact, scientifically unprovable if it is not capable of being verified experimentally in the laboratory. Evolutionism is therefore not as scientific as we have been led to believe. Its evidence is as speculative as man's occupation of America via the Bering Strait, as we shall soon see. The best that can be shown is that it all may have happened, not that it did happen. To the chagrin of some, the truth is that evolutionism is largely based on faith and dogma.

Christianity and Judaism are not unique as carriers of a belief in creation. The American Indians relate it to the Great Spirit and ancient religions such as Buddhism, Hinduism, Shintoism, Islam have similar views of how man and the universe came into being.

The real culprit in disseminating theory as fact is the popular press, which often has a bill of goods to sell. *Time-Life Books*, for one glaring example, advertises its *The Emergence of Man* series of volumes with colorful mockups and paintings of imaginary ape-men. "Today," they glibly expound, "that creature who first ventured to raise himself above the other animals no longer exists; he has become you. Unique. Set apart from the two million other species living on the planet by a thumb that makes your hand a precision tool . . . by a knee that 'locks' you in a comfortable position . . . and by your capacity for abstract thought and speech. . ."

"In the introductory volume, *Life Before Man*, you'll experience the stranger-than-science-fiction excitement of the earth's beginnings," the ads exhort. "You'll feel a sense of immediacy and visual adventure in the incredibly life-like pictorial technique, photo-painting. Over one hundred illustrations and fact-filled text give you fascinating new answers to age-old questions about the evolution of man." And the first volume of all this sophisticated, worldly wisdom costs only $5.95, with many more volumes to come, of course.

What did Cayce say on the subject and does it make any sense? With emphatic words, he rejects the Darwinian theory of evolution. Man was created as man, he insists, some ten and a half million years ago, a date far older than generally recognized.

". . . when the first of life in flesh form appeared in earth's plane, the entity among those making the first appearance in the form of man; or, when the development reached such that the Universal Forces then created the soul-man, the entity then among the first born of the sons of man." (*Case #4609–1*)

"Man was made in the beginning," he said in another discourse, "as ruler over those elements which were prepared in the earth plane for his needs. When the plane became such that man was capable of being sustained by the forces and conditions . . . upon the face of the earth plane, man appeared . . . and in man there is found . . . all that may be found without, in the whole . . . earth plane; and other than that, the *soul of man* is that which makes him above all animal, vegetable, mineral kingdoms of the earth plane. Man *did not* descend from the monkey, but he has evolved, resuscitation, you see, from time to time—here a little, there a little, line upon line . . . All souls were created in the beginning, and are finding their way back to whence they came." And he adds, "Man is man, and God's order of creation . . ." (*Case #3744-4*)

Now new evidence has come to light partially supporting what the sleeping seer had to say about the age of man. The National Geographic Society reported in 1972 and 1973 that expeditions had made startling finds in the African desert of Kenya. Uncovered were the oldest known nearly complete skull of early man and two thigh bones. Although fragmented, the fossils were found in volcanic ash dating to 2.6 million years ago. The skull is considered most remarkable for its size and resemblance to modern man's—lacking the preorbital ridges and sloping brow found in *Homo erectus* and *Australopithecus*, presumed to be our more recent apelike ancestors. The significance of the discoveries is that it could lead to a reappraisal of orthodox scientific thinking about the age—some two million years—and evolution of man, for the thigh bones are those of a walking man, not a loping ape. Parallel developments are therefore suggested much earlier.

Another recent find, reported by the Associated Press in 1974, is that of parts of jawbones with teeth found in Ethiopia. The fragments are believed to be the oldest members of the human family ever found—four million years of age. This is twice as old as the previous oldest specimen, an elbow uncovered in the same region in 1965. Leg bones uncovered in Ethiopia in 1973 indicate man was walking upright at least three million years ago, long before "evolving hominids". The area was once a fertile plain, as Cayce indicated.

In 1975, Dr. Mary Leakey discovered in Tanzania jaws and teeth of eleven "modern man" types, dating to 3.7 million years ago, indicating separate lineage.

The finds raise some fundamental questions about the evolution of man. Formerly it was believed that *Australopithecus* developed primarily during the Pleistocene ice-sheet period, which began only two million years ago. And it still leaves open the problem of how that evolution took place and when the "man-ape" developed into hominids walking upright with ground-living habits and a larger brain, if indeed he did.

Supporting the Cayce readings even further about the age of man, ten and a half million years ago for the coming of the perfect race, is the reexamination of fossil fragments found in Italy back in 1872. Modern American anthropologists have surprisingly learned that they are in fact human bones, not fossils, and date to some ten million years ago. If correct, this would place man far beyond the widely accepted age of evolving man-apes—no more than two million years ago.

Probably the most sensational claim for the age of man was that made by Dr. Johannes Heurezeler of Basle University, Switzerland, in 1958. He found a complete skeleton six hundred feet down in an Italian coal mine. By conventional geological and anthropological methods it was established as ten million years of age. More startling still to many, Dr. Heurezeler concluded that the creature was not an ape form but altogether humanoid. "It had a short face as opposed to the snout of an ape; it had no 'simian gap', a characteristic space in apes between adjacent teeth and the canines; the front teeth are fixed steeply in the jawbones, whereas the front teeth in apes point out, the canine teeth are smaller than the big canine teeth in apes; the chin is rounded on the front instead of sharp; the nostrils are ascending instead of being flat as in apes; the lower three molars are characteristic of man and not of the apes; a hole that carries a human nerve through the lower jawbone is present."

Granting that the man was indeed true man, one can only wonder about Dr. Heurezeler's dating. Could he have been a modern trapped by an earthquake? Yet the fossil was found near remarkably preserved remains of animals and plants known to be ten million years old: an otter, pig, antelope, mastodon, and parts of oak, gum and laurel trees—all relatively easy to date. The find is still taken lightly in most quarters.

After one hundred years, the Darwinian theory of evolution is just that—a theory. While some animals have evolved dramatically, there is still no proof that man has done so. No Chimpanzee, his nearest "living relative", has yet evolved into man. If this kind of evolution did take place, it should still be in process, and one can only ask, Where is the creature that presently is changing into man? If the theory of "genetic selection" is a fact, most infants today would surely be born with a strong right arm! There is not one missing link, but several missing links.

The California State Board of Education has voted to downgrade Darwin's theory in new science text books. The evidence is so slight it was called "speculative". At a conference in 1972, two top theologians and a scientist said that the concept of human evolution often is mistakenly taught as fact rather than theory. "Some scientists are as dogmatic about evolution as some preachers are about religion," complained anthropologist Margaret Mead. Dr. Colin Williams, dean of Yale Divinity School, criticized the "unbalanced teaching" of the evolutionary school of thought. And, said Dr. David Hubbard, president of Fuller Theological Seminary, "Much of it is almost crypto-theology."

Evolution may indeed be an idea whose time has gone. The old scenario runs something like this: Fourteen million years ago the first primate, *Ramapithecus*, showed up. Nine million years later, *Australopithecus*, still subhuman, but just possibly a tool-user, made his appearance. He developed into a "handyman" some three million years later. One million years ago *Homo erectus*, with his larger brain evolved enough to be considered human, after a fashion. Then came *Neanderthal*, the wise man and the first *Homo sapiens*, believed to have appeared about 200,000 years ago. Seventy thousand years ago he disappeared from Europe and was replaced by *Cro-Magnon* around 30,000 B.C.

It is now possible to trace our beginning back to at

least the 2.8 million-year-old bones uncovered by
Richard Leakey, son of the famous husband–wife team,
and probably to four million years. Although the brain
case of his find in Africa is small, "Its whole shape is
remarkably reminiscent of modern man's," he says.
"The leg bones are practically indistinguishable from
those of modern man." He believes man and ape lived
side by side although of one source.

Comments an article in orthodox *Reader's Digest*: "It
may be that we did not evolve from any of the
previously known human types, but descended in a
direct line of our own."

Human footprints alongside those of dinosaurs found
in the Paluxy River near Glenrose, Texas, support the
idea. They were men 8–9 feet tall. But dinosaurs were
extinct 130 million years ago!

Third Eye and Giants?

Cayce makes the extraordinary claim of a "third
eye", located in the center of the forehead of earliest,
prehistoric man. Moreover, there were "giants in the
earth in those days", before the coming of the perfect
race. Occult powers were commonplace because the pituitary gland was highly developed. Through it and the
third eye functioned the creative, psychic abilities of the
soul force, he asserted. Man had knowledge of events in
distant places and foreknowledge of things to come. But
as he drifted away from his spiritual source and purpose
and became more and more immersed in materiality, he
gradually lost the primary use of this gland and the third
eye, he said. The third eye vanished, but the pituitary
gland remains, although little evidence of ancient giants
or third eyes has been uncovered.

The pituitary is a small, pea-sized, reddish-gray mass
lodged near and connected to the brain. Each of its two
lobes had a special function. When the forward lobe is
over-active, the body is built up into gigantic form,
known as giantism. Diminished activity results in
various anomalies and mental defects. It is not known
to have any relationship to sight or a "third eye". Thus

Cayce, at best, can only be half-right.

But near the pituitary is the pineal gland, a strange body whose function has long been questioned. The most favored early belief was that it is a vestigal sense-organ, probably originally an eye. It is present in several species of mammals—fish, lizards, man. The sphenodon reptile of Stephen Island, New Zealand, thirty inches long and unchanged for 250 million years, is an ordinary lizard except that it has a third eye, and this parietal eye is related to the pineal gland in mammals, not the pituitary. Rudimentary in most vertebrates, its function is largely unknown. Scholars believe it to be derived through evolution from a third eye, although this is uncertain.

The pineal is also currently thought to be an endocrinal regulator of sexual activities in mammals, but the evidence for this is even more uncertain.

Thus Cayce said the third eye was connected with the pituitary gland while science says it is the pineal. And here he was caught in a crunch. In 1941, he was asked, "Medical science calls the glands at the base of the brain pituitary and the third eye pineal. Why have these names been reversed? Please explain."

"Their activity indicates that, from the angles of this study, these should be reversed," he answered.

He was pressed further. "Meaning we should reverse ours, or that medical science should?"

Answer: "To understand what is being given, reverse them! We are not telling medical science what to do! We are telling *you* what to do!" (*Case #281–54*)

Trapped in an untenable position, Cayce was obviously angered.

The Races of Man

Asia, and particularly the Middle-East, has long been regarded as the home of the human species. But today, Africa, not Asia, is favored as the most likely birthplace of man. From there he spread to other areas, known as the "Diffusion theory".

Cayce's version is almost totally different. "When

earth brought forth the seed in her season, and man
came in the earth plane as the lord of that in that sphere,
man appeared in five places then at once—the five
senses, the five reasons, the five spheres, the five
developments, the five nations." (*Case #5748-1*)

The readings unscientifically maintain that the five
races of physically perfect man entered the earth plane
in widely-placed locations. Namely: The black race in
Africa, the white in the Carpathian and Caucasian
Mountains of Southern Europe, the yellow in the Gobi
Desert of Mongolia, the brown in the sunken continent
of Lemuria in the Pacific, and the red race in the lost
continent of Atlantis. A few of the latter were also in
Southwestern United States and the Andes Mountains
of Peru.

Scholars long ago discarded the color identification
of the races as the governing factor. But new studies in
the evolution of pigmentation and resistance to disease
show that the hotter the climate the darker the skin.
Scientific American, in December, 1970, reported that
the evolution of skin color may be related to the require-
ment for calciferol, a hormone sometimes called vita-
min D, obtained from the sun's ultraviolet rays. An ac-
companying map shows the distribution of human skin
colors before the migrations of the sixteenth century.

Dark skin is believed to have protected the body
against over-production of calciferol, and the blacks
and browns are located in torrid Africa and the South
Pacific area. In Europe, on the other hand, man needed
all the ultraviolet rays he could get, especially in winter,
and thus developed unpigmented white skin. The medium light skin (yellow) is placed in China, Mongolia,
and Siberia. Medium skin (red) is located primarily in
North and South America. The map correlates well,
with some variation in surrounding areas, with Cayce's
version of the five races.

Say the readings: These races, "as has been given . . .
from their environs took on that as became necessary
for the meeting of these varying conditions under which
their personalities and individualities began to put on

form . . . as partakers of those things that brought about variations in . . . the outer presentation . . . or the skin, or the pigment that is presented in same." (*Case #364-9*)

In another discourse, Cayce said: "The needs of those in the north country (are) not the same as those in the torrid region. Hence, development comes to meet the needs in the various conditions under which man is placed. He (is) only using those laws that are ever and ever in existence in the plane . . ." (*Case #3744-4*)

The Europeans

The sudden departure of the *Neanderthals* from the European theater some 30,000 to 70,000 years ago, the almost instantaneous appearance and proliferation of the *Cro-Magnards*, and the absence of any immediate ancestors of modern man disrupts and jeopardizes the theory of evolution. To salvage it, Ales Hrdlicka, a noted anthropologist, proposed in 1930 the gradual replacement of the subhuman Neanderthals by the Cro-Magnons with their superior mentality and adaptability. But Hrdlicka also entertained a more promising and intriguing explanation of the sudden rise of the Cro-Magnard culture. It requires postulating an invasion of Europe during the peak of the glacial period by large numbers of a superior race coming from a motherland with a big population. He rejected the idea because there was no such land, and it appeared irrational that large numbers of people should be attracted to a Europe of glacial ice.

The upper limit of the first Cro-Magnards in Europe is consistently 30,000 years ago. Atlantis, Cayce says, suffered "the second period of disturbance" in 28,000 B.C., and many Atlanteans escaped the Great Deluge by emigrating to nearby highlands, including the Pyrenees Mountains between France and Spain, which may have been ice-free. If the Cro-Magnards are from Atlantis, it is understandable why they successfully succeeded the Neanderthals, and why their earliest appearance occurred in Western Europe rather than in the Near East.

Today, the autonomous Basque people of the Pyrenees are one of the mysteries of the continent. Many questions surround their culture and their origin. Fiercely independent, proud and patriotic, they speak an untraceable language wholly different from other European tongues, hold animal dances, and are noted as explorers, discoverers, and administrators. Even their music has a distinction of its own. All this is reminiscent of Cayce's story of the Atlanteans. Although the Basque are white and the Atlanteans supposedly were red, it is not improbable that the European fringes of Atlantis's population were of the white race.

Man the Artist

In the Pyrenees are also some of the world's oldest paintings, dating from 12,000 to 25,000 B.C. Far from crude, unimaginative splashes and scratches, these sophisticated works of art—some with three-dimensional affect—are not the creation of ignorant hunters but of skilled and sensitive artists.

Protected by caves and overhanging rock shelters, bisons, human figures in their finery, domestic scenes, are depicted in bright colors and fine sculpture. These works of man demonstrate beyond any doubt his creative instincts and abilities wherever he has been found, and at a rather early date. No member of the animal kingdom has yet produced any art, music, literature, or even a language.

Said Cayce: "That from the beginning there have been such (divine) influences upon the mind of man is seen not only in that termed Holy Writ, but in art, in music, in song, in verse, in prose. It is demonstrable in every walk of life, and has been through all ages." (*Case #5752–4*)

Again: "Man has a creative force from the divine, see? Man may misapply that own creative force, then become a destruction to self. Man's applying that force in that channel in which that is directed gives light, life, and abundance in every way and manner. Mind, the Builder." (*Case #900–227*)

One of the fundamental assumptions of prehistorians has for more than a century been that most of the cultural advances in ancient Europe came from the early civilizations of Egypt and Mesopotamia (Iraq) in Western Asia.

In Brittany, France, for instance, are the massive stone tomb monuments, some weighing more than forty tons, called "Fairies' Rock". Because of the great effort required to raise the forty-two slabs, scholars traditionally refused to credit them to the "barbaric" cultures of Europe. Instead, they attributed them to influences from the eastern Mediterranean.

Another example is that of copper metallurgy. It was supposed that this knowledge and practice had been transmitted to the Balkans of Europe from the Near East, as part of the diffusion theory from early Asia.

But now European tree-ring dating reveals ages that are pre-Asian. Tree-ring measurements have shown that carbon-14 dates are off by as much as 700 years, placing the date of the Fairies' tombs earlier than 4000 B.C., a millennium before monumental funerary architecture appeared in the eastern Mediterranean, and 1500 years before the accepted date of the pyramids. Metallurgy, too, may have been independently invented and used in the Balkans and possibly Spain before it was in Greece.

The lesson is that science has consistently undervalued the originality and creativity of prehistoric Europeans. Diffusion has been overplayed. "When the textbooks are rewritten, as they will have to be," writes Colin Renfrew in *Scientific American*, "it is not only the European dates that will be altered. A shift in the basic nature of archaeological reasoning is necessary."

An American writer–scientist turned archaeologist, Alexander Marschack, a research fellow at Harvard's Peabody Museum of Archaeology and Ethnology, stunned the scientific world in 1972 with claims that man's artistic abilities go back to 135,000 years ago, perhaps 300,000. This antedates the Neanderthals by thousands of years and clashes with the idea that man's evolution has moved from animal-like, sub-intelligent brains to today's sophistication, and with the image of early man as the simple toolmaker, not the artistic creature.

Marschack has analyzed the symbols on an ox rib found in France, apparently enscribed by early hunters. It is the oldest engraved bone uncovered. "Not only was man abstracting, he was making images of abstractions," Marschack says in a paper delivered before the American Anthropological Association in Toronto. "We are pushing back the concepts of 'roots of civilization' thousands of years." The symbols suggest pre-writing and some kind of language and communication, he believes.

"For 100 years, archaeologists have been saying that fully human culture began with *Homo sapiens*. But now we're seeing that *Cro-Magnon* and still earlier man were using ritual, ceremony, symbols. Earlier man may have made true art," Marschack says. "We don't know. But he did engrave intentionally. No one could have made those parallel lines unintentionally."

Predictably, his findings and conclusions stirred up a hornets' nest among scholars, and they are still a long way from Cayce's claim of 10½ million years for creative man.

In 1975, a Columbia University anthropologist, Dr. Ralph Solecki and a French colleague concluded that a Neanderthal grave site uncovered in Iraq in 1963 contained clusters of medicinal shrub and flower pollen. The find reinforces the idea that the Neanderthal were not hulking, brutish creatures without esthetic appreciation. The cave, dating to about 60,000 years ago, suggests ritual burials and a belief in some kind of life after death. Repeated findings of flint tools and body ornaments ritually arranged indicate religious beliefs. "The coincidence," Solecki concedes, "does raise speculation about the extent of human spirit in Neanderthals."

On History and Prehistory

One of the fashionable myths of our time is that the Bible is myth, folklore, or a work of pure fiction. It may indeed contain some of these elements, but the charges are much too sweeping for a blanket indictment. Much of it is symbolic and esoteric, and therefore escapes the minds of those who require a literal translation.

Edgar Cayce had a lot to say about the Scriptures, and he again and again vouchsafed their authenticity, often casting new light on shadowy passages. The readings uphold in principle if not in detail the Genesis story, the Great Flood, the Virgin Birth, the Resurrection, and many other Old and New Testament teachings. Most, of course, cannot be proved or disproved.

Man knows a great deal about history, but his knowledge of prehistory is scanty and necessarily speculative. The facts are hard to come by, and postulations are essential. Unfortunately, they too often turn into dogma. The Genesis story in general and the episode of Noah and the Ark in particular, have long been discredited by literal-minded skeptics.

The Bible relates how Noah was decreed by God because of the sins of man to construct a boat 300 cubits long and 50 cubits wide in preparation for a coming deluge. It reportedly landed on Mount Ararat. Noah's ship would therefore be 450 feet by 75 feet, a cubit being one and a half feet.

The Cayce records reveal the following: "Before that the entity lived in the earth during those periods when the peoples were separated that prepared for the preserving of the activities in the earth. The entity was the son of Ham (Canaan) that laughed at the weakness of the grandfather. Thus the entity was one of those who occupied the ark, or was in the ark during that period. After the journeys in the ark, the entity set out activities in definite conditions for the establishing of groups in various portions of the land." (*Case #3345-1*) Other readings also corroborate the story of Noah and the Flood.

For years, rumors and unconfirmed reports have been coming out of Turkey and the Soviet Union of the remains of a ship high up on the northwest slope of Mt. Ararat in Turkey. Now it appears that the ice-locked object may come to the light of day.

First spotted in the 1800's, the dark, oblong splotch has been seen by Pan American flight crews and passengers on numerous occasions. And a U.S. investigating team, Scientific Exploration Archaeological Research (SEARCH), is planning to uncover it.

In the summer of 1970, its group of scholars set out for the 17,000-foot climb up Ararat with a hot idea: melt the ice. But suddenly the one-and-a-half million dollar expedition was cancelled by the Turkish government. Internal political unrest made the establishment nervous about the status of the quo; Mt. Ararat was placed off-limits.

Already discovered, however, were some hard facts. The strange object, buried under seventy feet of a stagnant glacier, was calculated by ice-depth measuring equipment which can detect solid matter, to be 450 feet long and 75 feet wide, the exact size of the Ark. Odd pieces of wood were found nearby—one, sealed with tar, was estimated to be 4–5000 years old. But carbon-14 tests show an age of only 1000 to 1700 years, although carbon-14 has been found to be not altogether reliable, especially for wood preserved in ice.

There are no trees within a radius of 500 miles, says Professor Franklin Turrell, a plant biochemist. "To find wood at the 17,000-foot level of a mountain should not have happened." One splinter was found in salty ice crystal!

Happily, the SEARCH expedition is now on again and work will continue as planned, if it can raise the finances. Another team, led by Dr. Henry Morris of San Diego, also plans a trek of arkeologists to Ararat.

But a large discrepancy exists in Cayce's date for the Great Flood; he seems to place it in 28,000 B.C. Bible scholars calculate the time as about 4300 B.C., well within the range of the tested piece of wood. Only the uncovering of the remains can prove or disprove the antiquity of these dates. Hopefully, new evidence will soon be forthcoming about the truth or untruth of Noah and his zoo. Complicating the problem, however, is the fact that there were a number of ice ages and therefore several possible flood periods, geologically as well as according to Cayce.

The Druids of Stonehenge

Numerous theories and innumerable speculations have grown around the mystical Druids of England, Scotland, and Wales. At some unknown date in ancient history, they set up monumental altar stones and instituted temple services, the most famous site being Stonehenge in England. Some scholars believe the circular formation was used as a lunar calendar.

One theory, for which there is some archaeological evidence, maintains that a Lost Tribe of Israel made its way via the Balkans of Europe to the British Isles. The people, known as the Druids, reached their zenith in the last century B.C. Invasion and conquest by the Romans brought about their decline.

Cayce once made a comment that supports the theory. "Before that we find the entity was in the

English land when the peoples from the Holy Land were taking hold on the land. The entity was with those people who sought refuge . . . who had come from even the temple watch in Jerusalem, who had established the outer courts or the temple for individual service and activity as well as the altars which have long since been torn away, and yet there are evidences (remaining) . . . (stones) set up in the form of a court, and an inner court for (those) who would learn of the Lord." (*Case #5276-1*)

A deeply religious people who taught the immortality and transmigration of the soul, the secret order still exists there and in the U.S., Australia, New Zealand, Germany, and Scandinavia. Unhappily, they kept no records and have no written history, and Cayce gave no dates or other details.

But in 1944 he did give a revealing reading for an entity, ". . . in the Holy Land when there were those breakings-up in the periods when the land was being sacked by the Chaldeans and Persians . . . among those groups who escaped in the ships (and) settled in portions of the English land near what is now Salisbury, and there builded those altars that were to represent the dedications of individuals to a service of a living God." (*Case #3645-1*)

This would place the date between 2100 and 1600 B.C. Stonehenge, situated eight miles north of Salisbury, has been dated by radioactive determination at 1848 B.C., plus or minus 275 years. The structures show a Mediterranean influence that was not confirmed until 1953.

The First Americans

The Cayce records make the astonishing and "scientifically insupportable" claim that the American Southeest was the native home—along with Atlantis and the Andean Mountains of Peru—of the people of the red race. Until recently, there was almost nothing to support that this is true other than circumstantial evidence.

On the other hand, one of the cherished doctrines of modern history is that the Americas were first populated by Asiatics from Siberia. By way of the Bering Strait off the tip of Alaska, men, women, children, and their dogs trudged across a land or an ice bridge some 10 to 25,000 years ago. The hypothesis is thickly pasted over scanty geographical, geological, and ethnological evidence. It's almost as though someone looked at the map and decided, "They musta' come that-a-way."

Since there is an absence of anthropoid ape forms in the Americas linking man to "his past", as in the Old World, the original American Indians *had* to come from some place else. Siberians, like some Indians, are round-headed, black-haired, high-cheek-boned, and the two continents are barely fifty miles apart. To this wealth of non-evidence is added a few undated chipped stones and flint points similar to those used by the early South-westerners of perhaps 23,000 B.C. The discovery of mammoth tusks in frozen muck at the bottom of an Alaskan cliff shows that these Mongol newcomers "probably" stampeded the beasts over the precipice to kill them and feast in abundant luxury.

That briefly sums up the case for the Bering Strait thesis. As one authority was frank enough to write, "So, for much of our information . . . we will have to fall back on the archaeologists' imagination." And he admits, "The trail of these first Americans across Alaska and Canada has vanished as completely as their frozen breath in the arctic air." Eskimo prehistory dates from certain to only 2–3000 B.C., and it sheds "little light on the first people to come into North America," writes another. "There remains a gap between the Eskimo and earliest Americans."

The adult human bones found in Arctic Canada date to only 500 B.C. No very early campsites have been uncovered, no revealing artifacts discovered. Eskimos are not Indians, but Mongoloids, and American "Indians" are neither Mongoloid nor Indian, a misnomer the people of India still resent. Eskimos are late-comers to this continent, no doubt via the Bering Strait, and few in number. American red Indians are long-heads, not round-heads as are the Polynesian-type brown Indians. Siberians aren't red, but yellow, and the claim of "genetic drift" in so short a time is highly unlikely, if not impossible. The American red Indians are a distinct people, and they have no tradition of coming from the north.

It is entirely probable that a few hardy South-westerners wandered northward into Canada and Alaska in search of large game and lost some spear points, for 10,000 years ago, southern mastodons were rapidly being killed off for food. Moreover, the oldest find so far, that of the disputed hearthstones of a circular fireplace, stone tools and weapons in California's Mojave Desert, date to at least 100,000 years ago some experts think, far earlier than previously believed possible. Dr. Louis Leakey authenticated over 600 specimens as the work of man; others dispute this. New dating methods found human bones in the San Diego area to be 48,000 years old.

By the time of the last glaciation in 10,000 B.C., ice-sheets reached as far south as the Ohio Valley and probably North Carolina. Man could have been living in relative comfort in Mexico, Arizona, New Mexico, Nevada, Utah, as Cayce claims, throughout the entire ice ages of one to two million years ago and beyond, although parts of the area may have been under water at certain periods.

Said Cayce: ". . . in the land of now the Utah and Nevada forces, when the first peoples were separated into groups as families. The entity, then in the name Ulda . . . gave then much to the people in the manner of the way to prepare the dwellings for the mates, as the entity (was) one among the few who were successful in holding same to that view; that is, her own mate, see? . . . In the ruins as are found that have arisen, in the mounds and caves in the northwestern portion of New Mexico, may be seen some of the drawings the entity then made. Some ten million years ago." (*Case #2665-2*)

As for the brown Indians, Cayce said: "Before that we find the entity was in that land now known as the American, during those periods when there were the changes that had brought about the sinking of Mu or Lemuria (in the Pacific), or those peoples in the periods who had changed to what is now a portion of the Rocky Mountain area; Arizona, New Mexico, portions of Nevada and Utah." (*Case #851-2*)

The most mind-shaking find for the scientific world was revealed in November, 1973, demolishing the Trans-Siberian hypothesis beyond reclamation. Dr. Harold Malde of the U.S. Geological Survey reported the discovery in Central Mexico of man-made stone tools buried alongside camel and elephant bones dating 250,000 years old. There is no question that the implements are man-made, he declared before his distraught colleagues, and the date has been established by the latest testing methods. The artifacts are of a type not found in Europe and Asia until 40,000 years ago.

A heated debate will surely ensue, for scientific ears are attuned to the north, not to the south of the continent. The find is devastating because there were supposedly no people in Siberia 250,000 years ago and no bridge between the two land masses.

Times and ideas change, but as Steinbeck wrote, the people just keep going on and on.

As for genetics, Cayce once answered a question this way: "You have inherited most from yourself, not from family! The family is only a river through which it (the entity, the soul), flows!" (*Case #1233-1*)

The Mu of Lemuria

As though one "Lost Continent" were not enough, Cayce makes the almost incredible claim that there were two. Lemuria, he declared, lay in what is now the Pacific Ocean, and it stretched from the upper West Coast of the U.S. to the tip of South America. Inhabited by the peoples of the brown race, called the Mu, it was destroyed after the second of the great land upheavals, presumably 28,000 B.C., although the date is in doubt. Atlantis's final demise did not arrive until 10,700 B.C.

The following came as part of the answer to a question concerning the appearance of the earth's surface at the height of Atlantean civilization. "Then, with that portion, *then* the South Pacific, or Lemuria, began its disappearance—even before Atlantis, for the changes were brought about in the latter portion of that period, or what would be termed ten thousand seven hundred light years, or earth years, or present setting of those, as set by Amilius—or Adam." (*Case #364-4*)

In a later reading, he asserted: "In the one (life) before this, we find (the entity) in the days of the peoples coming from the waters in the submerged areas of the southern portion as is now of Peru, when the earth was divided, and the people began to inhabit the earth again. The entity (was) among those who succeeded in gaining the earth again. The entity among those who succeeded in gaining the higher grounds, and then in the name . . . Omrui and changed to Mosases; for the entity became the ruler and the guide, or the patriarch of that age and gave much assistance to the few as (were) gathered about the entity." (*Case #470-2*) Again, he said, "The entity (was) then among those that were the leaders of Ohums (in earliest Peru) when there was the breaking up of the deeps, and the lands disappeared and reappeared . . ." (*Case #2365-2*)

We have no further details on any part of a "Lemuria" disappearing and reappearing, but in 1966 *Science News* for April 9, reported the following: "Strange carved rock columns, shown on this week's front cover, some with writing on them, have been sighted by cameras six thousand feet under the sea off the coast of Peru. (Photo credit: Duke University)

"This unknown Atlantis of the Pacific lies too deep for exploration from a surface ship, said Dr. Robert J. Menzies, director of ocean research at the Duke University Marine Laboratory, Beaufort, North Carolina. A mobile deep-diving vehicle is needed for precise observation. Two upright columns, about two feet or more in diameter, were sighted extending five feet out of the mud. Two more had fallen down and were partially buried, and another angular squarish block was seen, said Dr. Menzies. The pieces were sighted from a surface ship carrying apparatus for lowering cameras to within a few feet of the ocean floor. The oceanographic cruise of the research vessel *Anton Brunn* lasted for six weeks off the coasts of Peru and Ecuador in the waters of the Milne–Edward Deep, a deep trench that drops off to almost 19,000 feet in places. The cruise was sponsored by the National Science Foundation."

The article goes on to indicate that there may have been a counterpart Atlantis named Lemuria in the Pacific. "The sunken columns are located about fifty-five miles off the city of Gallao, the port of Lima, capital of Peru. This is near the Ring of Fire, the zone of earthquakes and active volcanoes that encircles the Pacific Ocean. The area has once been covered by at least six hundred feet less of sea-water, about eleven thousand years ago, at the time of the great glaciers of the Ice Age, said Dr. Menzies. The area is now slowly sinking."

There had been other discoveries near the pillars, *Science News* pointed out. "Old Inca ruins have been found around that area, and civilizations predating the Incas by many years are now believed to have existed nearby." "But," said Menzies, "we did not find structures like these anywhere else. I have never seen anything like this before."

The find, of course, was quite by accident. The expedition was not searching for Lemuria; it was foraging for specimens of a small molusk. A thousand underwater photographs had been taken before it stumbled upon the sunken ruins.

The American Indians are unique. A biological quirk exists in the fact that they do not contain all the blood groups found in populations elsewhere. In Central and South America, all native tribes are of blood type O. In North America, they're largely O with 10–15 percent in group A. (Lemurians?) Siberians are high in O, but not exclusively; Hawaiians (Polynesians) are 61 percent A and 36 percent O types. There are no blood groups B or AB anywhere in the Americas as there are in most other parts of the world. The American Indians are a distinct people.

The First Aviators

Of all the incredible claims made by Cayce, none must have been more incredulous than his assertion that the ancient Atlanteans had aircraft. He indicated that natural gas was one of the first discoveries of early man, which is believable enough. But he claimed that by the time of the first catastrophe in 50,700 B.C., they were fabricating balloons from the hides of pachyderms, lifting them by gas, and eventually powering them by solar energy. Before and during the three continental disasters, fleeing Atlanteans took to the air in search of safety lands in Central and South America among other places.

"When the peoples of the nations gathered as one to defend self against the fowls of the air and beasts of the field, the entity among those who would be called an envoy to such gathering, (and came in the) lighter-than-air machines." (*Case #2749-1*)

In another reading, Cayce said: "There we find the entity was among those who were not only in what is now known as the Yucatan land, but also the Pyrenees and the Egyptian. For the manners of transportation, the manners of communications through the airships of that period were such as Ezekiel described of a much later date." (*Case #1859-1*)

Today, flying across the desolate plateau adjacent to the Nasca Valley in southern Peru, one may see a strange jumble of long, straight, criss-crossing lines and the design of a huge spider. Not far away are similar lines and the figure of a thunderbird engraved in the sandy soil. Although frequently seen by pilots, they were not seriously studied until 1941, when Drs. Paul Kosok and Maria Reiche investigated. The lines—some running for forty miles from nowhere to nowhere—were evidently for astronomical purposes and of pre-Inca orgin (2000 B.C. to A.D. 500?). Dr. Reiche found that some of the lines coincide with the solstices, others with the stars and the rising and setting of the sun.

Still masked in mystery is the meaning and purpose of the huge stylized bird, which is 400 feet long, and the somewhat smaller spider figure. They are presumed to be ceremonial shrines, for lack of a better explanation. But, canning the uncanny, their design can only be seen and determined from the air. A person on the ground would not recognize them as more than nonsensical ditches. Moreover, a similar huge figure, that of a man 180 feet long, has been found in Central Arizona, where Atlanteans also fled, says Cayce. Navajo tradition has it that the first emigrants arrived via air.

Since the designs are meaningful only from great height, the question arises, Did early man have aircraft? Were the symbols signs for navigators in search of unfamiliar landing places? Did the figures say, in effect, "This is the place"? For nearby are strange, flat, long strips that could be used as runways.

In Egypt, a model sailplane has been discovered that dates to the fourth century B.C. Futuristic in design, it bears a close resemblance to the American Hercules transport plane which has a distinctive reverse dihedral wing. Made of sycamore wood, the plane's tail has a span of 45 inches. Its discoverer, Dr. Kahlil Messiha, believes the early Egyptians were very advanced in certain areas, including elementary aeronautics. He is convinced that the find is a scale model of an actual plane or glider. Ancient Egyptian engineers always made models, he says, from funeral boats to war chariots.

Whatever the merits of his ideas, the Cairo Museum is placing the model plane on display.

Erich von Daniken and other writers on outer space have proposed that the Peruvian and similar oddities that have puzzled archaeologists and historians for years were created by visitors from other planets. One goes so far as to suggest that the visitors might have been earthmen of the distant future who returned to the past through some kind of imaginary "time machine". Another submits that even God was one of the astronauts.

There are indeed ancient rock paintings of men wearing flying helmets or sitting in aircraft. In Colombia, in South America, there is a gold artifact more than 1000 years old that bears a strong resemblance to a modern delta-wing jet fighter plane. The Book of Ezekiel speaks of flying creatures with wheels—interpreted by some to be flying saucers.

Far more likely than UFO's from outer space are solid earthmen from Atlantis looking for suitable lands of refuge.

Further support for the idea that the ancients had some sort of aircraft comes from the Piri Reis maps. Reis, a Turkish admiral and geographer of the sixteenth century, came into possession of nine Greek maps handed down from the time of Alexander the Great in the fourth century B.C. One shows the coasts of South America, Africa, and parts of Greenland and Antarctica which proved to be remarkably accurate and containing details later found to be true.

In combining the maps, Reis came up with a geography of the world dating 5000 years old designed by knowledgable cartographers who had evidently visited almost the entire earth. "But they contain data that go back thousands of years earlier than that," said M.I. Walters, a cartographer formerly with the U.S. Hydrographic Office, speaking at the Georgetown University Forum in 1956.

"We cannot understand how they could have been so accurate," submitted Navy Captain Arlington H. Mallery, author of *Lost America* and an authority on ancient maps. "Of course, in the first place, it was evident that there was little ice then. But secondly, they had a record, for example, of every mountain range in Northern Canada and Alaska—which the Army Map

Service did not have . . . They have since found them.
How were they able to do it? You will probably recall
the tradition of the Greeks of the airplane—maybe they
had the airplane. But the fact is that they did it. Not
only that, they knew their longitude absolutely correctly. This was something that we did not know ourselves until about two centuries ago.''

Mallery's contentions and the validity of the maps are
still in dispute.

The Great Wall of Peru

Another of the many riddles of South America is the
purpose of seemingly useless walls. One runs for fifty
miles from 1500 feet above sea level in the Andes Mountains down to the desert lowlands of the Pacific coast.
Called the Great Wall of Peru, it is made of stone and
adobe and originally rose to a height of 15 feet from a
base of about the same width. Of ancient, but uncertain, date, it was not discovered until 1931, from an
airplane. The remains of similar walls, much shorter in
length, have also been found in the dry valleys south of
Lima.

Speculation among scholars above the Great Wall has
centered on its probable use as a protection against
enemies by the pre-Inca *Chimu* tribe. Some think it
simply marked a boundary. So little has been discovered
that the mystery of Peru's wall is still with us.

The Cayce readings offer an unanticipated but practical explanation. ''In the one before this, we find in the
Peruvian forces, when the now called Incas set the rule
in that land, and the entity then the builder of the con-
duits through the mountains . . . (thus) that innate
desire to find the source through which all forms of con-
duits are prepared in the present day . . . May be applied, however, in later life in the form of drainage to
lands.'' (*Case #2888-2*)

The Incas were an advanced agricultural people
10,000 years ago, suggests Cayce, and it is known that
their highly developed farming system required extensive irrigation for a wide variety of vegetable crops. It

was the Incas, Cayce said, who built the "walls" across the mountains. Interestingly, they grew maize long before the North American tribes, indicating migration to the southwest, as Cayce claims.

The Death Ray

At the height of the Atlantean civilization, Cayce contends it had reached a scientific development superior in many ways to our own, and among its achievements was the "death ray", powered by solar energy. When the "forces of Belial" usurped power and overthrew the government of the "Children of the Law of One", the lethal beam was used against them. The *Tuaoi Stone* or *Firestone* that supplied solar energy to the land became known among the people as "The Terrible Crystals", for they were used also as a means of coercion and punishment for dissenters.

When Cayce submitted the idea of a "death ray" forty years ago, it must have appeared fantastic—the notion was in the private domain of "Superman". But in 1960, the laser beam was invented, and a new weapon came into the hands of the military. Today, the Pentagon is developing a laser beam bomb powerful enough to vaporize an enemy tank hundreds of miles away. Ruby lasers may toast a piece of bread 1000 miles distant. The Army is considering the laser's capabilities against air attack; the Air Force is researching laser use against guided missiles. All is done in the name of "defense" and "national security", but such weapons can also be used offensively. Military and aerospace agencies are expected to spend some $317 million annually in the next five years on laser development.

Happily, scientists are now at work on more beneficial purposes, such as surgery in repairing damaged eyes, gathering atmospheric data for weather forecasting, studying the earth's surface to detect possible earthquakes, capping teeth so that they are decay-resistant, removing tattoos and birth marks.

"Laser" is an acronym for Light Amplification by Stimulated Emission of Radiation. The process takes undiffused light and projects its very high heat in a small beam with the expenditure of enormous energy.

None of this proves that Cayce was right about the Atlanteans having the death ray—only that it was possible. The "Great Crystals" magnified the rays of the sun and broadcast the electricity via radio waves throughout the land. They were the main source of power, only later adapted to a lethal beam when the "forces of evil" took over.

On Changes in the Earth

Of all Cayce's strange utterances, none is more persistent than that the legendary continent of Atlantis was a fact. In 700 Life Readings given from 1923 to 1944, he insisted that a high civilization reached its peak there about 10,700 B.C. Amazingly enough, they are internally consistent and without contradiction. Because of the sins of the people, the country was finally destroyed after three major land upheavals, around 9700.

The much maligned Atlantean theory makes possible a different approach to the numerous problems which are basic to the sciences of history, archaeology, anthropology, and ethnology. If Atlantis ever proves to have been a reality, consternation will surely prevail in the scientific community. Traditional tenets on the development and dispersion of the human race would be demolished. History would be turned upside down, geography stunned, and anthropology would have to be restructured. Perhaps this is why resistance to the theory is so widespread. Too many scholars have staked their claim and their careers in opposition to the Atlantean idea.

Atlantis as a fact, for instance, would undermine the hypothesis of the permanency of the oceans, which explains why oceanography and geology cling to negative attitudes toward a sunken continent. If a land so vast were actually destroyed at a time geologically close to the present, serious consideration would have to be given to the causes and the possibility of the repetition of similar catastrophes. It is not an inviting thought for orthodox science. Yet a sweet aroma of diversity is seeping through the chinks of the scientific establishment.

In 1940, Cayce went so far as to claim that "Poseidia will be among the first portions of Atlantis to rise again. Expect it in '68 and '69; not so far away!" (*Case #958–3*) The Bahamas and the British West Indies, especially the area of the Bimini Islands off the east coast of Florida, would reveal evidence of the sunken island which was once part of Atlantis.

In 1968 and 1969, Dr. Manson Valentine, a former Yale zoologist, Count Pino Turolla, an amateur archaeologist and photographer, Charles Berlitz, a deep-sea diver and grandson of the famous linguist, and other researchers did discover man-made structures near Bimini and Andros Islands off the coast of Miami. Changing ocean currents and receding sands exposed the artifacts in relatively shallow waters. Remains of apparent stone buildings, walls, gigantic steps, a causeway, marble sculpture, stone discs set in a pattern were sighted and pictures were taken. Most compelling of all were forty-four marble columns in a circular formation—some standing, some toppled over. Carbon-14 dating placed the aged around 10,000 B.C. The finds, not yet recovered, are still being debated.

Also in 1969, scientists on a Duke University research ship reported finding continental granite in the area. Said Dr. Bruce Heezen: "The occurrence of light-colored granite rocks may support an old theory that a continent formerly existed in the region . . . and may represent the core of a subsided, lost continent." A granite base would have to be there to support such a land mass.

Dr. Valentine, who is also an anthropologist, said in 1973 he believes Cuba and the West Indies are remnants of the lost continent, which stretched from the American east coast as far north as the Potomac River to Britain, France, Spain and to the Azores. He thinks the land went under about 9500 B.C. after a fourth and final cataclysm, and that it was peopled by a powerful nation of highly civilized and intelligent beings who knew how to neutralize the pull of gravity in order to lift into place blocks of stone 20 feet long, 10 feet wide, and 3 feet thick. The stones, cemented with mortar, are of a different type than presently found on nearby islands, and the workmanship bears no resemblance to the stonework of local natives.

Valentine's date and location correlate well with Cayce's, who said Atlantis was finally inundated in 9700, after three catastrophes, and that the land compared in size to Europe and Russia combined. It stretched from the east coast to the Gulf of Mexico, to parts of Central and South America, and as far as the Mediterranean Sea. This would include Cuba and the Azores, although Cayce does not mention them.

But Valentine's version becomes highly questionable when he raises the possibility of population infusions from other planets of the solar system to explain the Atlantean's high civilization. A more substantive problem is why a greater amount of it was not transplanted to the lands of refuge. The answer can only lie in another question. How much of our scientific knowledge and achievement could we take with us in the event of nuclear holocaust? The average layman could not so much as fabricate a light bulb.

The search for the Lost Continent of Atlantis continues. In 1977, Charles Berlitz reported the location of a 500-foot pyramid in the Bermuda triangle.

The Outer Edge of Atlantis

The continent of Atlantis, Cayce claimed, lay in the North Atlantic Ocean, extending from the U.S. Eastern Seaboard to the Mediterranean Sea. "What is now the central portion of this country, or the Mississippi basin, was then all in the ocean; only the plateau was existent, or the regions that are now portions of Nevada, Utah, and Arizona formed the greater part of what we know as the United States. That along the Atlantic board formed the outer portion then, or the lowlands of Atlantis.'' (*Case #364-13*)

This was possible and credible up to a point. The northeastern central and midwestern regions are known to have once been inundated with glaciers and water. But what of the long stretch of coastal land around and south of New York City? Geologists have always believed that the outer reaches of eastern and midwestern glaciation were 500 miles away from the southern states. The south should have been dry land and therefore a solid part of Atlantis.

Cayce's statements of the lowlands appeared questionable until April of 1973, when two geologists found evidence of Ice Age glaciation in North Carolina mountains. James Burkland and Loren Raymond of Appalachian State University said their discovery in the northwest part of the state was "The first positive evidence of glaciation south of New York.'' The Catskill Mountains of New York were presumed to have been the most southerly point in that region.

"Nobody else made the discovery because they generally accepted the theories that denied the existence of glaciers this far south and because of the remoteness of the area," they stated. The sites, on Grandfather Mountain near Linville, N.C., are 4600 feet above sea level and an hour's walk from the nearest road. The finds, dating to at least 13,000 B.C., consist of a scraped basin and thirty to forty twelve-inch parallel grooves averaging a foot long in rock outcroppings. The discovery, they predict, will necessitate the rewriting of geology text books.

The entire Southern Seaboard could indeed have been the lowlands of Atlantis. When the ice-sheets melted, it takes little imagination to visualize what might have happened. There is evidence that North Carolina's outer banks once extended farther seaward.

In the spring of 1973, Dr. David E. Pettry of Virginia Tech reported research on hundreds of craters in the coastal area from New Jersey to Florida. Measuring from 200 feet to a mile in diameter, people have been living in and around them for years without realizing they are craters. They are especially prevalent along Virginia's eastern shore. The National Aeronautics and Space Administration also became interested when high-altitude photographs in 1971 showed how common and widespread are the formations along the coast.

Those nearest the water may still be forming, Pettry notes, and all researchers "have agreed that water has something to do with or is responsible for the formations." J. Holland Scott, Jr., of NASA, believes the craters probably are due "to some tidal phenomenon". Pettry thinks modern technology has nearly ruled out the possibility the depressions are caused by the settling of the land. He maintains the eastern shore was under as much as a mile of water in prehistoric times.

Further evidence for Atlantis may come from a joint U.S.-U.S.S.R. oceanographic research team exploring the geologic origins of volcanic Iceland in the far North Atlantic. But its members have different views. Most American scientists believe the island and its adjacent sea floor were created by material flowing from the earth's interior at the fracture zone that runs the length of the mid-Atlantic ridge. Soviet scholars tend toward the hypothesis that Iceland and the surrounding sea floor represent part of a subsided continent that once linked Greenland and Europe. Seismic data already gathered suggests that crustal material around Iceland is, said one Russian, "a more nearly continental type than a mid-ocean type."

Widely held theories support the idea that the sea floors are slowly and steadily moving away from the mid-ocean ridges and in the process moving continents and shaping mountains. If true, the idea that it did, in fact, happen in the past is no longer so absurd.

Adding to the accumulating evidence in favor of an Atlantis, is the uncovering of a human skull by underwater archaeologist William Cockrell, in the waters of southwestern Florida. Dating to 10,000 years ago, it is the oldest evidence of man found in the eastern U.S., predating the Mound Builders by several thousand years.

Across the Atlantic in the Aegean Sea, a hot debate waxes around the research and discoveries of Professor Spyridon don Marinatos, director of the Greek Department of Antiquities. He has uncovered on the volcanic island of Santorini near Crete magnificent paintings of a blue monkey, a dancing girl, red, white and black native stone, 3500 ceramic pots, sculptured bulls, and delicately wrought frescoes which surpass all others found in the Mediterranean region. Undoubtedly the work of a high civilization long since lost, they have been dated to about 1400 B.C. This is much more recent than Cayce's claim for the last Atlantean disaster—starting in 10,700 B.C. and apparently culminating in 9700. Jacques Cousteau made an exploration of Santorini in 1976.

But samplings of the ocean bed nearby revealed there were at least two volcanic explosions, the first dating to 25,000 B.C., coming close to Cayce's 28,000 B.C. for the second cataclysm. Arguments persist not only over the dates, but over whether Santorini may have been part of the Minoan or Plato's Atlantean empire. Both could be true, although Plato's date matches Cayce's 10,000 B.C., the nature of the people, and their decline.

Carbon-14 dates of 9-10,000 B.C. keep popping up around the world, suggesting a universal catastrophe. Deep sea sediments in the Atlantic suddenly changed from warm to cold water deposits; thousands of Pleistocene animals were quickly frozen in Siberia and Alaska; tons of boulder gravel were mysteriously moved and deposited in many unlikely places. Something very strange seemingly took place on this planet around 10,000 B.C.

Power from the Sun

Forty years ago, the Virginia Beach seer predicted that the energy source of the future lay in solar, not atomic, power. The continent of Atlantis with its advanced culture and technology received its energy from the sun, he claimed, and it was broadcast across the land via wireless power stations. The mechanism of the central power plant was known as The Great Crystals.

"The concentration through the prisms or glass . . . was in such a manner that it acted upon the instruments that were connected with the various modes of travel, through induction methods—that made much the character of control as the remote control through radio vibrations or directions would be in the present day; through the manner of the force that was impelled from the stone acted upon the motivating forces in the crafts themselves . . ." (*Case #440–5*)

All this sounds like something out of a science-fiction novel. Nevertheless, substantial progress is now being made in solar energy research and development. The whole of mankind produces in one year 30,000 times less energy than our planet receives from the sun in the same period. Every year the sun pours down on us a hundred times more energy than is contained in our accumulated and prospected reserves of coal, oil, gas, and all other organic fuels combined. World power needs could be met by the amount of solar energy that falls on a few tens of thousands of square kilometers—a fraction of the deserts of Central Asia.

Soviet physicist A. F. Ioffe has discovered in the seemingly unspectacular crystal of the semi-conductor the prototype of future solar installations, destined in time, he believes, to change the concept of power engineering. Already in the experimental stages are solar motors for desalting water, running refrigerators, air conditioners, ovens, driers, ice-making machines, and the pulsed irradiation of seeds with concentrated sunlight which substantially raises crop yields.

Engineers at the University of Arizona have designed and built a sun-powered heating system which they believe will have "international significance" and "be a showcase for the world". Largest of its kind, it will heat up to 8000 square feet of space.

The solar collectors look like venetian blinds set in a rectangular frame 80 feet long and 16 feet wide, covered on both sides with heavy, ordinary glass panes. Electric blowers push the trapped, heated air through ducts. An electronic device adjusts the blinds to catch maximum sunlight. Called the ClearView Collector, smaller systems are already in use for private homes, but this is the first application on a scale useful for shopping malls and large office buildings. The units can be built into walls or roofs facing south.

Cayce's claim that the Atlantean method of transmitting power by broadcasting it across the land via something like radio waves must have sounded even more unbelievable than his crystals when he said it. But a similar proposal has been advanced by Peter E. Glaser, vice-president of Arthur D. Little, Inc., the Boston research firm. With the use of orbiting solar energy collectors, the sun's rays could be trapped nearly 24 hours a day, thus receiving 6 to 15 times the solar energy available at any terrestrial spot in the United States.

Glaser envisions it this way: "Two symmetrically arranged solar cell collectors convert solar energy directly to electricity. This electricity is fed to microwave generators to form an antenna between the collectors. The antenna directs a beam to a receiving station on earth where the microwave energy is safely and efficiently converted to electricity." With some improvements in our present technology, he believes transmitting efficiency from space to earth in any weather could reach 70 percent and be operational by the year 2000 and at a competitive price.

In some advanced countries, solar water heaters are now being commercially manufactured, solar cookers are in use, solar-powered ice plants are operating. Solar space heating—using water pipes to circulate heat from the roof throughout the house—is already competitive with electric heat in parts of the U.S. If prices for natural gas, oil and electricity continue to climb, solar heating could become competitive in almost every part of the country.

The means to convert the sun's rays to electric power

is here today. The main problem is an economic one
—the high initial installation cost and the financing of
it. Proponents of solar power long wanted the government to spend $100 million over the years, less than
what it will spend for the breeder reactor ($800 million)
with all its risks of accident, contamination, and waste
disposal. Three billion dollars have already been spent
on nuclear energy compared to just one million on solar
systems.

But the energy crisis forced a change in thinking. The
1977 Congress allocated $294 million for solar research,
a sizeable increase over the former $3.8 million. Still, it
is a miserly amount compared to the $1.8 billion
required for other energy studies, $3.8 billion for
nuclear, and the whopping $117 billion for the military.
Some experts recommend spending up to $3.5 billion
over the next fifteen years to develop solar power alone.
Unhappily, the U.S. has been less interested than Japan,
Australia, Israel, and the Soviet Union in exploiting its
commercial use. In July, 1973, 900 world scientists met
in Paris to discuss what has been accomplished in solar
energy research and application. In some areas, the U.S.
is lagging far behind. One reason is that major oil companies are buying up solar energy patents, presumably
to monopolize the market.

Sun power, so long neglected in deference to atomic
bombs, space flights, and military hardware, is at last
receiving some deserved attention. It is free, clean,
produces no waste or contamination, serves a practical,
useful purpose for everyone, and is unmonopolized.
Perhaps that's the hitch. Individual home heating would
burn the utilities.

United States Representative Morris Udall (D-Az.)
has called for federal funding of $20 to $30 million for a
demonstration plant. "We must stop this hemorrhage
of dollars flowing out of this country for foreign oil,"
he said. Ralph Nader is saying much the same thing; but
he believes solar energy should be controlled by the
public sector, not by private interests. A National
Science Foundation–NASA solar energy panel con-

cluded in 1972 that, "if solar development programs are successful, building heating could reach public use within five years, cooling in ten years . . . and electricity production in fifteen years."

Storms on the Sun

Predicting the future is always hazardous, for the free will of man is unpredictable, as Cayce himself often remarked. Given to making extreme assertions, the famous clairvoyant is most vulnerable in his prognostications. Yet most of them appear to have some basis in fact.

Speaking of sun spots, he once commented: "Yet when these (men) become as in defiance to that light which was commanded to march, to show forth the Lord's glory . . . do ye wonder then that there becomes reflected upon even the face of the sun those turmoils and strifes that have been and are the sin of man? . . . How does anger, jealousy, hate, animosity affect thee? Much as that confusion which is caused upon the earth by that which appears as a sun spot. The disruption of communication of all natures between men is what? . . . (The sun) reflects those turmoils that arise with thee, even as the earthquakes, even as wars and hates . . . What are the sun spots? A natural consequence of that turmoil which the sons of God reflect upon same." (*Case #5757-1*)

Hogwash? Mumbo-jumbo? Perhaps. But solar flares are on the increase, as are the sins of men as evidenced by widespread moral decay, deception, corruption and violence. Major storms on the sun exploded in October, 1968, August, 1972, and a record one in September, 1973, when Skylab instruments revealed a colossal flare-up that created a mushroom cloud ten times the size of the earth.

Some scientists believe they have found a relationship between sun spots and the number of icebergs in the Atlantic, the level of the Great Lakes, the quality of wine, the abundance of fish, the growth of trees. Records of the Hudson's Bay Company in Canada revealed that the number of fox, lynx, and rabbit pelts brought in by trappers followed the eleven-year sun spot cycles.

Responsible economists assert there is even a definite parallel between financial crisis and sun spots. Dr. Ellworth Huntington of Yale was a firm believer in the theory that changes in the sun affect not only the earth and its plants but human health and behavior. Others have found a surprising similarity between economic boom and bust and the sun spot cycles. Professor A. Tschijevsky, a Russian scientist, called attention to a striking correspondence between sun spots and human behavior as reflected in mass movements throughout history.

Dr. Harlan T. Stetson of Massachusetts Institute of Technology, a believer in the significance of sun spot activity as it affects the earth, has written cautiously, however, that "The question as to whether sun spots, through a subsequent chain of events, influence the behavior of living things on earth is always an intriguing idea. In our present state of knowledge, any discussion of this subject must still be regarded as highly speculative . . ." and he adds, "to know more about sun spots, what their far-reaching effects may be . . . is one of the pressing problems of science today."

Sun spots are known to emit electrical currents that affect power transmission, radio communications, the northern lights and possibly this planet's weather, wildlife, earthquakes and, surprisingly, human behavior. Scientists are studying their cause and predictability.

Granted that solar storms affect the earth, there is no way of knowing if human behavior affects the sun as Cayce claims.

Disturbances in New England

In 1932, Cayce made what appears to be an inordinately extravagant prediction. "All over the country we will find many physical changes of a minor or greater degree. The greater change, as we will find, in America, will be the North Atlantic Seaboard. Watch New York!" (*Case #311-8*)

"Portions of the now east coast of New York, or New York City itself, will in the main disappear," he proclaimed again in 1941. "This will be another generation, though, here; while the southern portions of Carolina, Georgia—these will disappear. This will be much sooner." (*Case #1152-11*)

Georgia and the Carolinas are still intact, and there is little to suggest they won't remain so despite some small loss of beach front. But in July, 1972, the *New York Times* reported the sudden rising of the North Atlantic sea level from Maine to Virginia. It has risen an unprecedented three inches in the past eight years, compared to the norm of about a foot per century in the past.

Rhode Island especially is shrinking in land area. A rise in sea level of four-tenths foot in the last forty years has covered up to 40 feet of coastline in some areas. The cause is believed to be either melting polar ice or sinking land, or both. One scientist sees the trend as a potential "castastrophe on low coastlines within thirty years." Others are less pessimistic and more hopeful it is only temporary.

Steacey D. Hicks, a physical oceanographer with the National Oceanic and Atmospheric Administration of the Department of Commerce, reported the findings. He believes that the continued rise at the present rate of three feet per century poses a problem to communities along the coast. "I stand by my findings 100 percent," he said, "but I don't believe there is anything to worry about in one man's life-time."

There has been increased seismic activity in eastern Canada, New England, Pennsylvania and New York in recent years. Earthquakes are not restricted to recognized zones, and New England is less well known for them, although eastern Pennsylvania has recorded thirty-one since records were started in 1727. In February, 1973, the area plus parts of New Jersey,

Delaware and Maryland were shaken by tremors, just a few hours after a major quake rocked the Kuril Islands in the Northern Pacific. L. Don Leet of Harvard is concerned that a big quake may very well hit some unpredictable seaboard spot before the century is over.

Mark Sbar of the Lamont–Doherty Geological Laboratory in Palisades, New York, concurs. "I have no doubt there will be a large earthquake on the East Coast. The question is when and where." Other seismologists and geologists agree. "I feel the area is overdue for a damaging shock," said one. Another added, "It is not a question of will there be an earthquake. It is a question of how bad it will be."

Upheavals in the West

The probability of a California quake of major proportions has long been recognized. But when Cayce in 1936 claimed that Salt Lake, Utah, and Nevada would also be affected, he appeared to be far off base. The two areas are hundreds of miles removed from California land faults and from each other.

"If there are the greater activities in the Vesuvius, or Pelee, then the southern coast of California—and the areas between Salt Lake and the southern portions of Nevada—may expect, within the three months following same, an inundation by the earthquakes." (*Case #270–35*) Another signal, he said, would be increased activity of Mt. Etna.

As improbable as the comments appear, they are no longer so unlikely. Seismologists and geologists have recently found "connecting dots" of unstable land areas between these locales. A nearly dormant tectonic plate under northern California and Oregon seems to link up to the Great Salt Lake Valley and to central Nevada.

The "dots" on a seismologist's map are much like those on a child's numbered puzzle; connecting them gives a meaningful picture of geological behavior and relationship, tying in with West Coast land faults. Two of these, the San Andreas and Hayward Faults, are presently showing serious slippage.

In October, 1972, Salt Lake had a short-lived but fairly strong tremor, rattling homes but causing no injuries. Nevada is the testing ground for nuclear devices.

The volcano Vesuvius, located in Italy, has been inactive since 1944, with minor eruptions that year and in 1929 and 1913. None of these compare with the gigantic eruption that destroyed Pompeii in A.D. 79. Mount Pelee on French Martinique Island southeast of Cuba, has been dormant since 1902. But Mount Etna in Sicily, inactive since 1951, has suddenly come to life; rumblings were reported in 1971 and 1975. Its last eruption occurred in 1928, when a new crater appeared. It also blew its top in 1911 and 1909. In February, 1974, Etna erupted violently for the first time in years. Geophysicists concur that there may be a relationship between earthquakes and volcanic eruptions, as Cayce suggests, but volcanologists suspect earthquakes affect volcanoes, not the reverse.

The late Professor Hugh Benioff of California's Institute of Technology and other experts have said the cities of Los Angeles and San Francisco could be hit by a major quake any day. The state straddles the great San Andreas land fault, a fracture 15 miles deep and 2000 miles long. Now it appears that Salt Lake and Nevada could also be affected.

Global Catastrophes

Much of what Cayce said makes a certain amount of sense, but he also made some fanciful, far-reaching predictions that have little basis in reality. Speaking of world-wide physical changes, he forecast that: "The greater portion of Japan must go into the sea. The upper portion of Europe will be changed as in the twinkling of an eye. Land will appear off the east coast of America. There will be the upheavals in the Arctic and in the Antarctic that will make for the eruptions of volcanoes in the torrid areas, and there will be the shifting then of the poles—so that where there has been those of a frigid or the semi-tropical will become the more tropical, and moss and fern will grow. And these will begin in those periods in '58 to '98, when these will be proclaimed as the periods when His light will be seen again in the clouds.'' (*Case #3976–15*; in 1934)

As for these dire predictions, one can only say the time is already half gone and none has happened yet. A volcanic island, Surtsy, did appear far off the east coast of Canada, in 1963, and Japan, sitting on a land fault, is subject to earthquakes. A major one occurred in Hokkaido Island in June of 1973, measuring 7.9 on the Richter scale, but Japan remains intact. Too, there is some evidence the North Pole is moving, but nothing has changed in the "upper portion of Europe".

Such global cataclyamic events appear highly unlikely if not impossible—although nothing is impossible. If they happened in the past, as Cayce asserts, could they happen again? Unfortunately, he did not indicate the source of the changes he predicts; and a new threat has recently arisen.

The suspicion that winters are getting colder is no longer mere suspicion among climatologists. For the past thirty years permanent snow on Baffin Island west of Greenland has expanded. Pack ice around Iceland in winter is increasing. Warmth-loving armadillos that once migrated northward into the Midwest are now retreating southward into Texas and Oklahoma, U.S. and Russian crop failures are on the increase because of climatic changes, especially rainfall.

A world-wide network of weather stations suggests worse is yet to come. It may get cold enough to permit glaciers to cover North America as far south as Long Island. The earth has experienced dramatic changes from warm to cold to warm again many times during past ice ages, and it could happen again, climatologists believe. The most reasonable explanation for the present phenomenon is that the amount of solar energy reaching the earth's surface is decreasing—and one of the suspected culprits is pollution.

Geochronologists, who study the chronology of the past as indicated by geologic data, confirm that the world is steadily cooling off. The best they hope for is a cool period lasting a few decades; the worst could last a hundred years and be as cold as during the Great Ice Age of millions of years ago.

"The earth has been cooling off since 1944," says Dr. Paul Damon, a University of Arizona geochronologist. "We're hoping the long cold trend won't be the case, though, but it could. That's why there is so much concern now." There was a warm period between A.D. 1200 and 1400, he says. Then a cold spell set in which lasted from 1400 to 1700's. After that the warmth came back until 1944. "There have been no huge declines in temperatures in the northern hemisphere since 1944," he relates, "but in the last five years satellite observations of snow fields show a southward drifting." The snow fields are in Canada, Alaska, Siberia, and Scandinavia.

"There have been freaky weather conditions and worldwide crop failures like wheat failures in Russia and drought in China and India," says Damon. A drop in temperature of only a couple degrees means an early winter, a short growing season, stunted cattle, food shortages.

The present erratic fluctuations of the earth's temperatures may be due to wobbling in its circuit around the sun, or possibly because of solar storms, others speculate. Whatever the cause, it may foreshadow a coming ice age. The world will experience another such period, Damon believes, but hopefully not for a few more thousand years. It's a question of temperature versus time. "If this is a long-term cold spell," Damon concludes, "it could be very, very serious." But such a cataclysm is far removed from Cayce's " '58 to '98".

In his propensity for extremes, he once told a man from Livingston, Montana, that his birthplace would one day be an economic center for the world and "have much to do with many, many nations!'' He went on to declare that Saskatchewan, Canada, the Pampas area of Argentina, portions of South Africa, and parts of Montana and Nevada "must feed the world!''

Livingston is a town of 6800 population and declining. Two-fifths of Montana is mountainous, and the valley community is in the midst of them in the south central part of the state. Altitudes reach to 13,000 feet; 5-6000 feet are common. With a cool climate, short summer and growing season, farming is not extensive outside of wheat, barley, oats and rye in the eastern plains region. The state is a heavy producer of cattle, dairy products, lumber, and minerals. Its prospects as a large scale food producer are not promising.

Across the border is Saskatchewan, the northern half of which is a wilderness of lakes and forests. But the southern part is a rich producer of high quality wheat and minerals.

For some unknown reason, Cayce skips over Idaho, next to Montana, and focuses on Nevada, 200 miles to the south. This arid state averages nine inches of precipitation, which is mostly snowfall in the mountains. A poor agriculture area, it is dominated by sheep and cattle ranches. Its prospects for feeding the world are worse than Montana's.

That bit of apparent fantasy is all the more wondrous when the enormous populations of Europe, the Soviet Union, India and China are considered, not to mention the U.S. and South America. If a shift of the poles should take place, as he predicts, with attendant climatic and geographic changes, the transportation problems alone would almost be prohibitive.

Cayce also blundered when he gave a positive answer to a question about physical changes in Alabama. "When will the changes begin?" he was asked.

Answer: "Thirty-six to thirty-eight."

Question: "What part of the state will be affected?"

Answer: "The northwestern part and the extreme southwestern part."

Question: "Are the physical changes in Alabama predicted for 1936–38 to be gradual or sudden changes?"

Answer: "Gradual."

Question: "What form will they take?"

Answer: ". . . This will take more of the form here in the change, as we find, through the sinking of portions, with the following up of the inundations by this overflow." (*Case #311-9-10*)

It has now been forty years and nothing of the sort has taken place.

Yet, for all Cayce's ominous predictions of coming earth and climate changes, something uncommon *is* occurring in our world. Not only is it growing colder; 1973 was a record year for windstorms and tornadoes in the U.S.—almost 1000. During the past twenty years the average was 659 compared to an average of 136 for the prior twenty years, 1915 to 1935. Something is surely upsetting the balance of nature.

Signalling coming land changes, Cayce predicted: "In the next few years, lands will appear in the Atlantic as well as in the Pacific." (*Case #1152-11*; 1941) He appeared to be wrong until the fall of 1973. A newborn volcanic island exploded to 160 feet height in the Iwo Jima chain 600 miles south of Tokyo. Unnamed to date, the island is still too hot to investigate. Surtsy Island in the Atlantic rose in 1963, although neither occurred "in the next few years" from 1941.

On Politics and Society

A fundamental idea of America's Founding Fathers was that "all men are created equal", but we have since become more enamored with Life, Liberty, and the Pursuit of Property. People are, from the reincarnationist view, not born equal, although they were created equal. They believe, and the Declaration of Independence implies, that all should have *equal opportunity*, a commodity sadly lacking for American blacks, browns, reds, poor whites, and women.

"There *cannot* be one measuring stick for the laborer . . ." said Cayce, "and another for the man behind the money changers. *All* are equal—not only under the material law but under the spiritual. And His laws, His will, will not come to naught!" (*Case #3976–18*; World Affairs Readings)

We are and always have been an unequal society. In income distribution, writes sociologist Herbert J. Gans of the Center for Policy Research, the poorest fifth of our population receives only 4 percent of the nation's annual income, and the next poorest fifth just 11 percent. Conversely, the richest fifth gets 45 percent, with the top 5 percent garnering over 20 percent of all national income. Worse still, one percent of the people control more than one-third of the country's wealth, and 2 percent of individual stockholders own two-thirds of personally held stocks in American corporations. The meek inherit the dearth.

The same imbalance exists in the corporate world. Of two million U.S. corporations, one-tenth of one percent controls well over half of total corporate assets; 1.1 percent controls 82 percent. At the other end of the scale, 94 percent of our small corporations own only 9 percent of total corporate assets.

"In the very nature, though, of a nation, a people, there are some fundamental principles upon which the economic and the soul life of a nation must be founded, if such a people, such a nation is to remain true to that which is the birthright of every soul . . ." says Cayce.

"For, the first law that has been given to man from the beginning is: 'Thou shalt have no other gods before me.' And when man has faltered, has altered that, which has deprived others from giving expression to that birthright, that command that has come to man throughout the ages, then there arises that which creates those things that are the fruits of the evil influences that are in the earth. Such as: hate, jealousy, avarice, and the like. These make for the creating of those conditions in all walks of life for power, for position, for the love of money and that it will bring in its associations in the lives of individuals. And, as there has been just this experience in the affairs of the nation as a nation, the nation as a nation is passing through that period when each soul must turn to that thought within of what is its relation to the Creative Forces in its experience . . ." (*Case #3976–14*)

Of all economic systems, capitalism is undoubtedly the best ever invented—for 19 percent of the people. Government statistics show that at age 65 and over, 23 percent of our senior citizens live on charity, 31 percent must still work to survive, 27 percent are dependent on relatives, pensions and meager Social Security, and 19 percent are retired and living on investments and savings. Perhaps this is why Americans have such a relatively low longevity rate. By the age of 68, only three years beyond retirement on Social Security, the average male is ready for his last place of abode. As a wit once said, Cannibalism gave way to capitalism when man discovered it was more profitable to exploit his neighbor than to eat him.

If America is to become a more stable society it must first become more egalitarian. And that begins with economics. The 1977 U.S. budget reveals that 45 percent of federal income derived from individuals and 14 percent from corporations, and the people ultimately pay that too. The poor pay a larger share of their income for taxes than do other income groups—50 percent per capita in direct and indirect taxes compared to 45 percent by those in the $50,000-up bracket. Low income groups are almost as unequal. Those earning $8-10,000 a year pay only four percent less of their income than those earning $25-50,000. Much of this is due to sales taxes and other "hidden" taxes.

The Great American Myth is rapidly fading. Rural people no longer hope that they can make it financially by saving up to buy a farm; agribusiness has taken over. Factory workers opening up a shop, store, or gas station are as likely to fail as to succeed. "Today these hopes have begun to disappear," writes Gans, "for the family farm is economically obsolete, the small store cannot compete with the chain, and the independent professions now consist more and more of salaried employees. Of course, there are still exceptions, and every year a few well-publicized individuals strike it rich, but their small number only proves the rule." Less than 1.5 percent are self-employed.

We are becoming a nation of hired hands. The people have lost control of their destiny to big business and big government. They who control the economy control the political, and they who control the political control the nation. Do we need to ask, Who owns America?

In a poll taken by the Illinois Chamber of Commerce of 3000 high school juniors and seniors on what they thought of American business, the answer was, Not much. The students believed that corporations make excessive profits, advertise inaccurately, and show little interest in the real needs of the people. On the other hand, the poll revealed that 60 percent of the students thought that labor unions were most responsible for raising the living standards of the average worker.

Dissatisfaction with our monopolizing economic system is even creeping into executive suites. In a survey of 2800 top-drawer businessmen by the American Management Association, 83 percent agreed that their attitudes toward business and success are changing to personal, private and family centered objectives. Forty-nine percent said that success for them is doing meaningful work no matter what the rewards. Thirty-four percent agreed that success is the realization of goals which may have little or no relation to career management.

The trend of turning away from seeking life fulfillment in a job is the result of the widening gap between the Puritan work ethic and its ineffectiveness in solving the social ills of the day. Urban decay, the revolt of youth, political and economic inequalities, unemployment and financial disasters are effects, not causes.

Because of its inherently prurient and competitive character, modern capitalism not only pits man against man but humanity against nature for the purpose of self-aggrandizement, of which Cayce had a lot to say—all negative. Liberal attempts to reform such a system are a gross illusion if not a cruel deception. The reforms are mere patch-work designed to maintain the established power structure and preserve the *status quo* with new, fancy plumbing. But leaks continue to break out in the boiler room. The economic empire builders cannot or will not reform to better serve the common good; the system is beyond redemption. Morally bankrupt, they can only stretch credulity to the explosive point. They don't have much to *quo* about, and they're running scared.

Said Cayce: "So, in the experience of those that have sent and made the conditions are greed, selfishness; that has been practiced in the minds, in the lives, in the experience of the nation. Think not any soul, 'Yea, that is true for the other fellow.' But it applies to Jim, to Tom, to those in ordinary walks of life . . . those that have wealth about them; *they* are the oppressors; yea, look within thine own heart! Hast thou not practiced the same?'' (*Case #3976-14*)

In a reading for a man who purportedly had an incarnation in ancient Persia, Cayce warned: "For, the entity was of that cult as would be termed of the capitalistic nature today; hence might made right." (*Case #2381-1*) And that is still the monopolists' philosophy if not their religion; Let us Prey.

A man in position to know once said: "The masters of the Government of the U.S. are the combined capitalists and manufacturers of the U.S. It is written on every page of the records of Congress." The speaker was Woodrow Wilson.

When corporations and a few wealthy individuals contribute millions of dollars to Congressional and Presidential campaigns, the Government is virtually up for sale. They are not doing it out of charity. When qualified people cannot run for office because they refuse to take special interest handouts, bribes, gratuities, our political system is up for grabs to the highest bidders. When appointments to high office, business favors and legal and legislative decisions are purchased behind the scenes by vested interests, our future is in jeopardy. The "Influence For Sale" signs are out. Are we becoming the land of the fee and the home of the knave?

All this explains why it is so difficult to get progressive, socially-conscious legislation through the Congress and the state houses. If it's not "socialistic" it's "inflationary" or "wasteful spending". What most Americans do not realize is that the U.S. in social well-being for the plain people is a backward country. It is the only industrialized nation without national health insurance. Most European countries, including the Communist ones, have near-free health care programs, adequate retirement pension plans, free higher education, especially West Germany and the Scandinavian states in the Western orbit. In Japan, auto workers retire at age 55 on good pensions, opening up jobs for the young.

America has lost its ideal. As Cayce once commented: "The ideals, the purposes that called the nation into being are well. It might be answered by saying that there needs to be on the part of each man, each woman, the adhering to those principles that caused the formulating of the American thought. Yet in the present there are seen many complex problems, many conditions that are at variance to the first cause or first principles; not only among groups and individuals in high places, both from the political and the economic situations, but the problems of labor–capital as well . . .

"And these as they are stressed become more and more of a problem. For with the very thought upon these things that are at variance to the principles of right, justice, mercy, peace, the right to worship according to the dictates of the conscience, as thought is given we find that power to the thought is created by the very mass of the thought itself, as well as conditions that become individual problems in the lives of the peoples of America.

"These are the problems not only as to who would be in power here or there, as to who would administer in this or that office, but the matter of the privilege to meet or worship according to those principles that have been set forth or proclaimed . . ." (*Case #3976–24*)

We need to decide very quickly what sort of country we want this to be, for America is in danger. Control is rapidly being transferred from local communities to absentee corporate boardrooms where the few decide the policies and the fate of the many. Millions of people depend helplessly on their whims. Through monopolistic mergers the public is losing the power to direct its own economic welfare, and in the process losing the means to control its political and social future.

The retail business is one of the few channels still open to the small, independent entrepreneur. Yet there were 19,000 fewer retail outlets in 1973 than there were in 1971. Each year 400,000 small firms go out of business, one-fourth in their first year, two-thirds within five years.

And therein hangs a tale of possible food shortages to come. A few giant corporations dominate food processing and are progressively taking over production and retailing. A paper written by the Agribusiness Accountability Project confirms the high concentration and declares that "its impacts already are being felt". "We have the most productive agriculture in the world, but we are faced with the real possibility of food shortages . . . In the middle of it, enjoying record profits . . . is corporate America." As far back as 1962, the Federal Trade Commission found that four big companies— Heinz, Campbell, Libby and Del Monte—garnered 80 percent of canning industry profits. Four companies control 91 percent of the cereal market; two dominate the soup industry; one, cheese.

Government studies in 1972, before the big rip-offs of recent years, disclosed overcharges at the consumer level of $483.9 million in meat packing plants, $256.7 million in milk, $47.8 million in soft drinks, $198 million in malt liquors, $191.9 million in bread and pastry products. After that came the whopping $10 billion highway oil robbery in 1974 and $20 billion in auto repairs in 1977. No end is in sight. Higher prices mean higher profits, and that's what the game is all about. By 1977, overcharges totaled $100 billion by F.T.C. reckoning.

Decades of public maltreatment are now coming to a head. Consumers have caught on to their exploitation, albeit belatedly. Polls show only 19 percent have great confidence in major corporations; 56 percent favor employee control of companies.

Freedom and the Press

Cayce was sometimes prone to say very little in a great many words. But he often said a great deal in very few words. "What is the spirit of America?" he once asked. "Most individuals proudly boast freedom. Freedom of what? When ye bind men's hearts and minds through various ways and manners, does it give them freedom of speech? Freedom of worship? Freedom from want?" (*Case #3976-29*)

The binding of men's hearts, and thereby their minds,

is an old story. Many of our conservative newspapers, magazines, book publishers and their political-science-fiction writers and columnists would make Hitler's propagandists sigh with envy in polluting the minds of otherwise intelligent people. Some journalists, of course, simply must stay on the payroll and fit their copy to the policies of the High Inca, or see it distorted by desk men and editors. Other far-rightists probably regard even the Founding Fathers as subversive.

"If the truth were ever known about the way in which government influence has been used by great corporations," wrote former Vice-President Henry A. Wallace in 1934, "public indignation would know no bounds." It has now been more than forty years and the public still doesn't know the massive extent of it except for occasional leaks that seep through the walls. The slanted press coverage was largely responsible for his 1972 landslide defeat, Senator George McGovern has said. "In reading the clippings . . . I don't know how we got 29 million votes." But most politicians and corporate public relations men know how to Beat the Press and Mace the Nation, as does the CIA in manipulating the news.

In a survey of the political position of newspapers in the mid-1960's, *The Columbia Journalism Review*, a leader in its field, reported that of 84 studies of bias in the news, 74 were pro-Republican and conservative in Republican papers and 7 were pro-Democratic in Democratic papers in their treatment of the news. Editorial copy, of course, is even more slanted to mold public opinion. In the 1968 presidential campaign between Nixon and Humphrey, a close and well-matched contest, a survey by *Editor and Publisher* showed that 634 newspapers with a circulation of 21 million copies supported Nixon while 146 with 4 million circulation backed Humphrey. All certainly knew of Nixon's past record. Despite the enormous propaganda effort, Nixon came in with little skin left on his teeth. The myth-information of the "New Nixon" worked.

Worse still, chain oligopolies rule our "freedom of speech". Of 1750 daily-newspaper cities, only 30 have competition; three-quarters are chains. What we need is more freedom from the press.

The Red Scare of McCarthyism in the 1950's was not a spontaneous, popular movement. Rather, it was and continues to be generated by economic and political cliques whose self-interest the hysteria served. They have a vested interest in keeping the people in ignorance, to form public opinion, not to inform the public. Misperceptions still persist, although some of the wind has been taken out of their bellicosity. It's not only what is printed; it is also *what is not printed*. Example: At a Baptist World Alliance conference in South America, the flags of the nations were brought on stage, and the Red Flag of communism received the greatest ovation. This disheartening kind of news never reaches the American public at large. Our prestige abroad has been declining alarmingly for twenty years, but few Americans know it. With the help of the CIA, we are becoming the most feared nation on earth.

So the people are trapped between the horns of a dilemma: censorship by government on one end and censorship by ownership on the other. The public gets the sharp needle of indoctrination from two sides. Yet in all fairness the news media are somewhat improved over past years. Journalists of the press and airways are weary and resentful of being hamstrung by blatant commercialism and right-wing intimidation. Exposures are becoming more frequent. Newsmen are rebelling. Said one editor of government efforts to control the news: "If a free press in abolished, there will be no freedom in our country, because no people have ever remained free for very long when the press has been intimidated or controlled by the government."

David Rintels, a television script writer and leader in the Writers Guild of America, told a senate committee that 81 percent of the nation's TV writers believe the medium presents a distorted picture of the U.S. political, economic and racial situation. "We are horrified because we know" viewers are seeing nothing but programs "deliberately designed to have no resemblance at all to reality; nonsense whose only purpose is to sell snake oil and laxatives and under-arm deodorants.''

But much of the fault lies with the people themselves. They don't demand serious programming and reporting. They don't do their homework. Few read important books, most don't read quality magazines, some don't even read newspapers except for the comics and the sports pages. Maybe they get what they deserve, but a democracy cannot function in a misinformed populace. Only their good common sense saves us from disaster.

Revolution in America?

"Every phase of human experience and human relationship must be taken into consideration . . .'' said Cayce. "For unless these are considered, there must eventually become a revolution in this country—and there will be a dividing of the sections as one against another. For these are the leveling means and manners to which men resort when there is plenty in *some* areas and a lack of the sustenance in the life of others.

"These are the manners in which such things as crime, riots and every nature of disturbance arise—in that those who are in authority are not considering every level, every phase of human activity and human experience.'' (*Case #3978–19*)

Cayce's warning appears more foreboding every day. In some backward, oppressed countries it is already a reality. The competitive, private profit-oriented system is being challenged from every side. Can capitalism meet the needs of the times? Although Cayce was a short-term pessimist he was a long-term optimist. The transition to a coming New Order "will begin in those periods in '58 to '98,'' he said. "When this period has been accomplished, then the New Era, the New Age is to begin.'' (*Case #3976–15*)

But the transition, if it comes, apparently will not be a painless one. Ridiculous and abhorrent as the idea of revolution in America must have sounded in 1938, it is not so unthinkable and unrealistic today, although nothing short of massive inflation/unemployment/ home foreclosures/bankruptcies could bring it about.

Under the Nixon Administration—those abominable showmen—among the first acts was the drawing up of contingency plans for the call-up of federal troops during domestic crises, ostensibly to cope with riots, demonstrations and other violations of "law and order". The President now had the power to implement the plans—coded "Garden Plot"—any time he felt an "emergency" existed. A classified document, known as the "Interdepartmental Action Plan for Civil Disturbances", outlines the responsibilities of the Defense and Justice departments in the event of mobilization, writes columnist Jack Anderson.

One can safely assume that some of the clandestine activities of the FBI, CIA, and the Pentagon are really aimed at thwarting any such uprising designed, not to overthrow the government, but to force change in the economic system, the Holy of Holies.

Senator Frank Church (Dem.–Idaho) spelled it all out when he said that under present laws, "the President may seize properties, mobilize production, seize commodities, institute martial law, seize control of all transportation and communications, regulate private capital, restrict travel, and in a host of particular and peculiar ways control the activities of all Americans." He has suggested that modern surveillance technology has taken us beyond the edge of no return. In 1976, some of the powers were revoked.

The story is told of President Eisenhower asking his Secretary of the Treasury, George Humphrey, if it were not possible for American businessmen to make some sacrifice in the interest of world peace.

"No," Humphrey replied candidly. "The American businessman believes in getting as much as he can while the getting is good."

"Maybe that's the trouble with businessmen, George," Eisenhower said seriously.

The "Sons of Belial" are back and in charge. We are indeed a nation of checks and balances; checks for the rich and balances due for the poor. The "children of the law of one" have largely abdicated their responsibilities in public affairs.

Yet, said Cayce in 1937: "In the United States at present there are some disturbing factors, especially those as related to activities of the nature pertaining to labor and capital in its various phases. Yet there need never be a fear on the part of capital that there will be much real disturbance until there is a more united effort on the part of any group, association or organization. And so long as capital is able to keep turmoils within the ranks of those that would bring strife through their very power rather than purpose, no great concerted effort may be expected that would play a definite part." (*Case #3976-17*)

But the winds of change are blowing in all directions. "There is a lesson of recent years that we may not have learned well," Secretary of the Treasury William E. Simon once told a group of businessmen. "Unless we heed it, our struggle to preserve the private enterprise system in America is doomed to fail." The lesson, of course, is, again, cosmetic reform to restore public faith in the American way of doing business. More concisely, capitalistic egonomics is an endangered species.

On International Affairs

Toynbee wrote that of twenty-two historic empires to collapse, nineteen fell from corruption within—not from forces without. The American empire has not collapsed into chaos, but it is standing on the precipice. With $300 billion invested in foreign countries, the economic czars will fight to the last American tax dollar and black and Southern redneck to protect "our interests abroad". Foreign policy is not made by the Department of State; it is made by those who profit from it—in brief, to defend and extend capitalism. That is why the government has to lie to the people. We hear a lot about "law and order" and petty "crime in the streets", but little of the massive crime in the suites. The motto is to tell the trufth, the holey trufth, and anything but the truth. Morals, integrity, fairness, live-and-let-live have almost nothing to do with foreign actions and reactions.

What is needed, Cayce once said, is more world-thinking. In another reading he predicted: "There has arisen and there is arising in the affairs and the experiences of man everywhere the necessity of there being not so much the consideration of a land as of all lands as a unit. For *mankind* is his brother, and thou *art* thy brother's keeper." (*Case #3976-16*)

Man may not yet be his brother's keeper but the "necessity" of global thinking is here.

Brian Urquhart, Assistant Secretary-General of the United Nations, has lived through many international crises. His vast experience since 1945 led him to say, "I suppose, in some ultimate sense, that if the U.N. is to succeed, the world has got to develop a greater sense of internationalism. But to reach it, most societies will have to pass through nationalism first—and many of them haven't even made that step yet. The politics of creating a U.N. majority is a constant reminder of how hard it is for us to work constructively together. It's also constant evidence that the United Nation's powers are restricted."

Cayce urged cooperation—not competition—again and again. But states do not suddenly change their character because they're in the U.N. Too many persist in their own national interests. "Unfortunately," said Urquhart, "that interest is sometimes a narrow and short-term self-interest."

Civilization as we know it is in a state of terroristic flux. Radical changes in perspective will have to be made if it is to survive.

"This culture in which we live is collapsing with enormous rapidity," warns British socio-economist Robert Theobald, author of a U.N. study on the future of the world. "The system within which we work is not functioning. The breakdown is going on rapidly, but we have built remarkably effective walls to keep from seeing it." Rather than fostering competition, he thinks "society should provide ways for cooperation," lest the structure where one has to kick his way to the top continue. He sees the 1970's as the crucial years.

Will man ever learn that he acts in his own best self-interest when he also helps others, for he is helping himself and his own?

But imperialism and neo-colonialism will never surrender peaceably. Although their time has gone, there is no limit—repeat no limit—to which the Sons of Belial will go to preserve their vested interests at home and abroad. It is a story as old as capitalism itself. Blunt speaking General Smedley D. Butler testified to that many years ago.

"I spent thirty-three years and four months in active service as a member of our country's most agile military force—the Marine Corps. I served in all commissioned ranks from a second Lieutenant to Major General. And during that period I spent most of my time being a high-class muscle man for big business, for Wall Street, and for the bankers. In short, I was a racketeer for capitalism . . .

"Thus I helped make Mexico and especially Tampico safe for American oil interests in 1915. I helped make Haiti and Cuba a decent place for the National City Bank boys to collect revenues in . . .

"I helped purify Nicaragua for the international banking house of Brown Brothers in 1909–12 . . . I brought light to the Dominican Republic for the American sugar interests in 1916 . . . I helped make Honduras 'right' for American fruit companies in 1903 . . . In China in 1927, I helped see to it that Standard Oil went its way unmolested.

"During those years I had, as the boys in the back room would say, a swell racket. I was rewarded with honors, medals, promotion. Looking back at it, I feel I might have given Al Capone a few hints. The best *he* could do was to operate his racket in three city districts. We Marines operated on three *continents*." Since then, thousands more American sons, husbands, fathers have died to make the world safe for Wall Street.

Today, such overt actions by the military would be incriminating and embarrassing to a government that likes to boast of its devotion to freedom, democracy, the self-determination of peoples. Such unsavory tasks are now given to the clandestine operations of the CIA.

But oppressed peoples will not tolerate oppression forever. Said Cayce: "From the conditions in other lands America must take warning. For to whom does the wealth belong? To whom do the possibilities of the land belong? Does it belong to those who have inherited it, to those who have been given the position of power? Or to those who have by their labor, by the sweat of their brow, *produced* same?'' *(Case #3978-19)*

"Capital labors as well . . ." he said. But *not* to the detriment of, but to the united effort of all *(Case # 1149)*

The Wall Street Mafia is still with us. And the Pentagon and CIA have made world heroes of Fidel, Mao, and Salvadore Allendé. The Castro régime was popular enough among Cubans that there was no hope of overthrowing it short of massive U.S. intervention. So much for the cliché about American non-interference in the affairs of other nations. The press and members of the parliament were bought off in Chile in an attempt to prevent the seating of Allendé, later killed. So much for the claim and American commitment to free speech and parliamentary democracy. What happened to Patrice Lumumba in the Congo, Prince Sihanouk in Cambodia, Ngo Dinh Diem in South Vietnam, Mossadeq in Iran, Juan Bosch in Dominican Republic, Arbenz in Guatemala demonstrates the true character of American policymakers and leadership. So much for our fondness of constitutional procedures and democratic control of the military/CIA.

No matter. The liberals and the reformers persist in the illusion that the modern capitalist Robbing Hoods can be redeemed. They are the hope-addicts of the day, for the system is beyond redemption. Respect for fundamental values, the Constitution, the Bill of Rights, the Declaration of Independence no more restrains the FBI at home than it does the CIA abroad.

But there is a way out of our dilemma, as we shall see. There is an alternative to capitalism, socialism, communism, and hopefully to fascism. We have seen the present and it doesn't work.

Decline of the Dollar

With inflation topless and the economy bottomless, Americans are suffering the pangs of over-exposure.

Of all America's difficulties, none is more enduring and dangerous than the potential fall of the dollar with its international implications. For most Western nations' currencies are inexorably hinged upon and tied to the dollar. What happens to it at home and abroad profoundly affects them all.

The causes of inflation are the creation of excess "paper money" that encourages its expansion, deficit financing, and willful price and interest increases unrestrained by a permissive government. Gold and silver are the real money, although true wealth is in goods and property, the things money will buy. Inflation balloons by running budget deficits and then creating the paper and credit dollars through the banking systems to make up the deficits.

The result is the same over and over again. The currency is debased in value as the money supply expands. Wages, prices, the cost of living rise. Unfortunately, people don't notice the money supply expanding; they see only the result—inflation—because they feel it where it hurts, in the pocketbook.

No end is in sight. The dollar will continue to weaken and gold and silver will continue to rise, temporary fluctuations aside, because of a lack of confidence in funny money. Yet the occupants of the White House and leaders of most other Western nations advocate revamping the international monetary system along non-gold lines; most simply don't have enough gold. Those that do, like South Africa and the Soviet Union, are sitting at the end of the rainbow.

Added to the economic mismanagement in Washington are wasteful, non-productive military spending, high interest rates, a protectionist and subservient Congress coerced into erecting trade barriers and exchange controls, a 600-billion dollar overhang in Europe, trade deficits, tax loopholes for corporations and the rich. The emerging picture is of an America foundering in stormy seas, unsure of where it's going or how to get there. This is why Europeans are so concerned about the true value of the dollar and what is going on in America.

It started back in April, 1933, when Franklin

Roosevelt took the dollar off the gold standard in order to manipulate and profit *vis-à-vis* the British pound and the French franc. The move delayed but did not resolve the problems of international currencies, and they are still with us today. Capitalist quarrels and economic warfare continue.

Roosevelt's destruction of the London Economic Conference in 1933 can be paralleled with Nixon's handling of a pressing international stabilization; they followed a policy of benign neglect of a highly vulnerable dollar. But there is one vital difference today. In 1933 the national treasury had a huge surplus; now it is not only virtually empty but in horrendous debt, living off borrowed money, i.e., Government bonds and Treasury notes.

In 1938, Cayce spoke to these complex and little understood problems. ". . . there must come, first, a stabilization of the monetary unit. There must come then the exchange of commodities or of trade in a way and manner in which not merely sections, not merely distinctions made of one portion of the land against another, but *all* are taken into consideration. Unless this is done, turmoils and strifes will arise." (*Case #3976-19*)

In 1940, he warned: "When thou hast gathered thy hoards of the earth together, and have entrusted them to the keeping of those who are wastrels, what has been and is the result in thy own experience? Want and need has come to thy hand!" (*Case #3976-25*) Are we living in the last of the Good Old Days?

Again in 1943, in answer to a question about "an international currency or an international stabilization of exchange values," he replied: "This too will be worked toward. It will be a long, long time before established. There may indeed be another war over just such conditions, but it'll be a step in the right direction—in the attempts in bringing peace at this time." (*Case #3976-28*)

It has indeed been a long, long time, and the problem has not yet been resolved. The Bretton Woods Conference of 1944 merely plastered over the cracks in the dike. Quick-fixes will not suffice to curb world-wide inflation, and citizens are now feeling the impact of years of neglect. "If nothing is done," one report of experts says, "there is grave danger that the international monetary system will degenerate into groups of conflicting currency blocs long before an agreement is reached on international monetary reform." With the failures of the International Monetary Fund meetings in recent years, the light at the end of the night is at best only flickering. Economist Eliot Janeway has cautioned that merely modifying exchange rates is no longer a viable solution to the problems. "Only a multinational political agreement can be of any use," he believes.

So the capitalist world's Number One continuing crisis goes on. The United States has successively devalued the dollar in attempts to pacify the situation. European banks and governments are loaded with questionable currencies. Speculators have in the past dumped dollars abroad out of a lack of confidence in the U.S., and gold cannonaded out of sight. Diamonds, silver, art, goods and property are in increasing demand. Ruinous inflation and world depression are real threats, and the former can be worse than the latter. We may one day be reduced to eating tossed greenback salad.

That is tasteless enough, but the suspicion in Europe is that the U.S. is happy to dump its paper dollars on allied governments: the chief beneficiaries are American speculators and conglomerates, who may use the acquired foreign funds to start another wave of investments, thereby dominating their economies even more. This is a highly sensitive sore point with many nations around the world, including a friend so close as Canada. The American Empire is repelling its best allies. Fifty billion dollars in loans by U.S. banks to lesser developed countries, to keep them from going socialist, doesn't help if much proves uncollectable.

Cayce once made a curious comment no longer difficult to place in context. "As ye have seen those in lowly places raised to those of power in the political, in the machinery of nations' activities, so shall ye see those in high places reduced and calling on the waters of darkness to cover them . . . the rottenness of those that have ministered in places will be brought to light, and turmoils and strifes shall enter." (*Case # 3976–15*)

As the pessimist said to the optimist, Have a nice doomsday! Things will get worse before they get better!

But all is not Boom, Gloom, and Doom. A ray of light is in sight, if Cayce is correct. His coming New Order may be at hand, and we will explore it at some length in the sections ahead.

The New Society

The average consumer, trapped in the sinkhole of expensive credit, pays dearly for the fringe benefits of America's affluent society. The tragic result of the rapid rise in installment buying is the concurrent increase in consumer fraud and deceit. Laws too often have been written to protect the seller, not the buyer.

In 1978, personal installment debt in the U.S. amounted to a staggering $424 billion. In 1975 it was $191 billion. Our vaunted high standard of living is founded on the tenuous ground of dangerously loose credit and soft dollars. We are in hock to an economic elite of absentee corporate owners: mortgage banks ($680 billion), insurance companies, loan associations, finance companies. The bucks stop there.

In the end it is always the consumer who pays and pays. *Caveat emptor* (let the buyer beware) is now the rule of the game. The federal government, if it is to preserve the system, must sooner or later establish some mechanism to protect the public from the untouchables in executive suites or lose the game. Changing the rules may help, but it will not keep the wolves from gobbling up the rabbits.

Lewis Engman, Chairman of the Federal Trade Commission, in a courageous speech once declared: "The simple fact is that for vast and increasing numbers of consumers with valid complaints there is nothing to be done—after two hours of haranguing the salesman, the supervisor, the department chief, the customer service girl and the store manager—other than to kick the dog, yell at his children, and curse his wife."

Engman believes, correctly, that the militant consumer movement is no passing phenomenon. It has already achieved some small victories and no doubt will continue to do so. But it cannot make over the system, although gallant men like Ralph Nader and John Gardner are trying to hold back the tide of political collusion, fraudulent schemes, and shoddy merchandise. Other public interest groups, such as the Consumers Federation of America, Credit Union National Association, and The Cooperative League of the U.S.A., have been aware of and attacking the problems for decades. Only the latter two have a different perspective and offer a real alternative. And on this Cayce had something important to say.

"While there will not be the reversal of the capitalistic system," he predicted in 1941, on which he may yet prove to be wrong, "there is to be the establishment more and more of the cooperative basis—in local, state, county, national and international activities. Cooperation must form the basis of activities, such as has been indicated here, and is to be applied not only in the home, but in corporations, in mines, in manufacturing in the nations—more and more. There will be the greater abilities, the greater possibilities, not of America becoming again as the land to which others flee, but Americans must go to the other lands and carry cooperation with them!" (*Case #2533-2*)

Of all Cayce's suggestions, few carry more impact than this solution to the economic ills that have plagued mankind for so many centuries. He apparently foresees a mixed economy with cooperatives dominating big business and utilities, leaving small business to the individual and true, free, unsubsidized enterprise.

Co-ops were around long before Cayce, but their rapid growth has taken place only in recent years. Profit and non-profit consumers and producers organizations are now flourishing across this country and abroad. New farm cooperatives are thriving in the fertile soil of the South. Food stores, pharmacies, clinics, eye glass dispensaries, garages, stores, pharmacies, clinics, eye glass dispensaries, garages, bakeries, drug, variety, furniture and department stores are owned and operated by the consumers themselves, not for profit but as a public service. There are almost 1000 electric and hundreds of telephone cooperatives in the U.S., and the Congress recently passed a co-op bank bill to facilitate loans.

The co-op idea is being exported to other countries. Credit Union National Association, based in Madison, Wisconsin, is helping under-developed peoples to form their own lending institutions with low interest rates in Latin America, Africa, Asia. There are 320 credit unions with 400,000 members in Peru alone. Worldwide, there are more than 57,000 credit unions with $30 billion in assets serving 44 million members. In the U.S., there are now 23,000, of which 1375 are church sponsored, reaching a total of one out of every four families. In Denmark, half the population belongs to co-operatives of one kind or another.

The Cooperative League is helping peoples in foreign countries to operate their own farms, poultry ranches, wool weaving industries, fishing fleets, processing plants. The growing movement gives large numbers of people meaningful participation and opportunity through ownership to become masters of their destinies rather than cogs in a system dominated by a small, powerful elite. No other alternative, state socialism included, offers so much freedom, equality, dignity, and abundance. Even in the well-to-do, mixed-economy nations of Europe and Scandinavia, strong co-op organizations have a sobering, levelling effect on private industries and the power cliques—they keep them honest —and the small, independent business man still thrives.

Buying Clubs are Sprouting!

A subtle evolution is taking hold in America's market place. Frustrated consumers, outraged by gyrating food prices, are discovering they have an alternative to complaining to store managers and boycotting and picketing supermarkets. Increasing numbers of cornered home-makers are turning to co-op buying clubs. Current interest in food co-ops is the highest it has been since the Great Depression.

New neighborhood, church and community clubs have bloomed in New York, Boston, Chicago, Sacramento, Tucson and other cities. The reasons are many, but polls reveal that Americans have lost confidence in the way business conducts its affairs—sinking to the lowest level since the 1930's.

In Las Vegas, housewives on a symposium panel told an audience of 100 of the nation's leading nutritionists that they didn't believe what they are told in food advertising and were losing faith in the government's ability to keep watch over the industry.

Buying clubs have advantages over co-op food stores. They don't require large capital investment and can be started over-night by as few as thirty families with no operating expenses. They are taking root in churches, fraternal organizations, colleges, neighborhoods. Every Friday morning, Albert Johnson, a social worker in Chicago's Lawndale Community, makes a trip to two or three wholesalers and produce jobbers to pick up orders for members of a club he started in 1971. Volunteers then weigh the potatoes and other bulk items, cut the meat to order, sort the eggs, fruit and vegetables in empty rooms they use as headquarters. By noon, housewives are filtering in to pick up their prepaid orders, and save up to 30 percent on some of their purchases.

Not far away, 76-year-old Paul Horvat of Wilmette set up 200 clubs serving 45,000 persons, many of them elderly. His clubs buy directly from farmers on some items. He not only lowered prices; he was given the Memorial Award of the Center for Science in the Public Interest for his "unique contribution toward improving the quality of the American diet."

In the end, it's a matter of public need versus private greed; of millions for the few and misery for millions.

The cooperative idea is creating a new faith in the capability of the young, the old, the disenchanted, the ordinary people who just like to save money to participate in a piece of the action: One person, one vote, regardless of the number of shares a member may hold in a large operation. Just as importantly, it is bringing a feeling of independence, purpose, and responsibility when they are most needed in our society. Consumer /employee-owned enterprises offer a democratic alternative and an opportunity to build a cohesive sense of community.

But the retail outlets cannot slay the food giants until they coordinate with co-op growers, as Cayce once implied. And this is no easy task. There is a natural confrontation and conflict of interest between buyer and seller. The buyer wants to buy as cheaply as possible; the seller wants to sell at the highest price possible. Even co-op farms must make a profit, since it is their members' livelihood. The co-op store is a non-profit public service; any profit goes to members.

In the Scandinavian countries, the problem was solved by cooperation and coordination. Some stores simply combined with the growers in one co-op. Others affiliated with and counseled with the growers. In both cases, the cooperative farm had a guaranteed market at a guaranteed price for a guaranteed amount of produce, and the store had a guaranteed source of supply at a fair price. Some are chain operations.

Most political systems will work once the concentration of wealth and power is removed from the private domain of the few. The solution rests in power from the bottom up, not from the top down.

Said Cayce: "For as has ever been . . . all phases of man's relationship to his fellow man, and those as represented in material, mental or spiritual capital, should be made a matter of education or knowledge to the general public. And as this is more consistently and persistently done . . . there will be the greater cooperation—whether it be in the banker, in the lawyer, the doctor, the merchant, or the government; or as related to capital or labor; for all of these in their basic principles are one. Cooperation is that ever needed and to be stressed . . ." (*Case #1151–24*)

Again: "Principles must carry through to the laboring man, whether it is the one that is felling the log, or the man that is the rough finisher, or he that sweeps up the floor! Don't think that the man at the top can take it off or out of the lives of the laborers and get away with it! He can't! Conditions are such that when honesty is carried through, it is the position to coordinate and cooperate all the way through. *That* is the cry of the country. It is the need of *all* business." *(Case # 257–182)*

But was Cayce referring to the cooperative movement? No matter. Co-ops are still a manifestation of cooperation and coordination at their highest level.

Sociologist Richard Quinney of Brown University argues that our delinquent society produces lawless juveniles; the gross inequalities in the distribution of wealth and power give rise to stresses that lead to violence and crime. "American capitalism is undergoing a severe crisis, and no solution to the crime problem will work without changing America's economic structure."

Freemasonary and the New Order

One of Cayce's improbable predictions concerns the coming New Order: it would be based on religious principles. Economically, his forecast is believable enough, for it is founded on the cooperative, not the competitive impulse in man. But when he made the following statement he seems far afield indeed. "For with the changes that will be wrought, Americanism—the ism—with the universal thought that is expressed and manifested in the brotherhood of man into group thought, expressed by the Masonic Order, will be the eventual rule in the settlement of affairs in the world. Not that the world is to become a Masonic order, but the principles that are embraced in same will be the basis upon which the new order of peace is to be established in '44 and '45." *(Case #1152–11;* 1931)

Cayce was correct in that World War II came to an end and those years saw the formation and ratification of the United Nations charter, setting new standards for the behavior of nations, although they have not been lived up to by the formers themselves. But his reference to Freemasonary appears unrealistic, considering today's moral climate.

The guiding principles of the ancient and secret order of Freemasonary are the wisdom and the necessity of personal integrity and stability; truthfulness and uprightness of character, purity and holiness of life. Spiritually motivated in its origins, its ideas are honesty, dignity, brotherly love, charity, unity, service to God and man. A true Freemason, wrote one 150 years ago, "would be just if there were no laws, human or divine, except those which were written in his heart by the finger of his Creator."

The profound, esoteric religious significance of Freemasonary is not generally publicized. William Wilmshurst, Past Master, Past Provincial Grand Registrar of West Yorks, England, wrote in his work, *The Masonic Initiation*: "The observant Masonic student is made aware by the formula used at Lodge-closing, that by some great Warden of life and death each soul is called into this objective world to labour upon itself, and is in due course summoned from it to rest from its labours and enter into subjective celestial refreshment, until once again it is called to labour." He speaks of the great rhythm of life and death, and how "the soul in the course of its career weaves and wears out many bodies" until such time as its work is completed and it is "made a pillar in the House of God and no more goes out."

A clear reference to reincarnation, it is difficult to imagine at present this fundamental belief playing any part in a new socio-economic political system. Politicians generally are not overly inclined to strong moral or religious views. They have almost completely lost the confidence of the American people—45 percent of the voters did not go to the polls in 1972 elections, before the White House of ill repute was fully exposed. In 1974 elections, only 38 percent bothered to vote. Political leaders would, however, be compelled to reconsider some of their misdeeds if persuaded that they would have to pay the price for them in another life. But this seems nigh impossible so long as the power structure is able to keep a majority of the people fooled. P. T. Barnum is America's greatest philosopher.

Yet, improbable as it seems, could it all happen as Cayce predicted? The key year in many of his prognostications is 1998. Then the New Order will begin, and it will be worldwide. Drastic geologic and socioeconomic changes will have taken place. There will be less of wars and nations peacefully "will carry on their trade one with another," he said. New breakthroughs in science, technology, and religion will benefit man everywhere.

In 1998, he predicted more than once, we may find a great deal of the activities as have been wrought by the gradual changes that are coming about. These are at the periods when the cycle of the solar activity, or the years, are related to the sun's passage through the various spheres of activity, and are apparently tantamount to the change between the Piscean and the Aquarian Age. This is a gradual, not a cataclysmic, activity in the experience of the earth in this period, said Cayce.

American-Soviet Friendship

In 1933, Cayce made what must have been a shocking statement to many of his adherents. The world was in the mire of the Great Depression, Stalin was purging Communist officials, liquidating the *kulaks*, and browbeating the churches into near extinction. Yet Cayce said: "On Russia's religious development will come the greater hope of the world. Then that one, or group, that is closer in its relationships may fare the better in the gradual changes and final settlement of conditions as to the rule of the world." (*Case #3976-10*)

The official Communist party line has long maintained that religion is the consolation of the ignorant, "the opiate of the masses". But, alas, as Soviet education has increased so has the interest in spiritual matters, and the Party is worried. The Russian newspaper, *Pravda*, has carried articles and editorials on the best methods of fighting resurging religion in the U.S.S.R. It complains that even some Party officials observe religious practices. Just as dangerous, it says, is the stubborn survival of religion in the armed forces, among students and Young Communist League members.

The Russian people's search for spiritual food is

manifest in their love of poetry, now booming, and the increasing spread of underground religious literature. Despite the earlier closing of churches, mosques and synagogues, baptisms, weddings and funerals are still being held in the 11,000 remaining open institutions. Sixty million Russians reportedly believe in God, sixty years of official atheism notwithstanding, and they are apparently on the increase. More portentous, their scientists' interest in psychic phenomena may lead to astonishing and unexpected results, and jar them out of some of their intellectual ruts. "The Soviet Union is experiencing a significant religious revival," one atheist defector declared.

While Cayce's remark may not be so absurd as it first sounded, it is still a long way from actuality. A leading Latin American Communist once told a religious missionary there, "Christianity offers man what communism offers, and much more because it promises a blessed future after death. You have much more to offer than we have. Yet we will win and you will lose because we believe what we preach and you don't."

Equally startling is Cayce's comment in 1944 clarifying the first. "In Russia there comes the hope of the world, not as that sometimes termed the Communistic, of the Bolshevistic; No! But freedom, freedom! that each man will live for his fellow man! The principle has been born. It will take years for it to be crystallized, but out of Russia comes again the hope of the world. Guided by what? That friendship with the nation that hath even set on its present monetary unit, In God We Trust." (*Case #3976-29*)

We may have our doubts about the extent of Russian freedom, but today these remarks no longer appear so patently ridiculous. Trade is on the increase—in 1973 it was seven times that of 1970. By 1977 it had climbed to three billion dollars. They need our grain, we need their raw materials. In 1972, 66,000 U.S. tourists visited the Soviet Union, compared to 12,000 in 1962. To encourage this, the new Russian passenger liner, *Mikhail Lernmontov*, is now cutting the waves between Leningrad and New York with 700 one-class passages for only $383. It has no hope of cutting a profit for years to come.

A new U.S. and U.S.S.R. Joint Commission on Scientific and Technical Cooperation recently approved twenty-five programs of research in six general areas: energy, computer applications to management, agriculture, micro-biology, chemical catalysis, and water resources. Coordination will include exchange of scientists and technical information, joint research, testing and development, and special arrangements between U.S. and U.S.S.R. agencies and companies. General Motors negotiated for an estimated $2-billion truck manufacturing facility in Siberia. Monsanto Chemical has signed a $100-million contract. A construction firm will build four ammonia plants in the U.S.S.R.

At Star City near Moscow, Russian cosmonauts are learning "American". At Batavia, Illinois, Soviet physicists helped inaugurate a new high-powered cyclotron. Hopefully, agreements can be reached on military reductions, expenditures that are far too costly for both sides. Détente is coming, not out of friendship but out of necessity. The arms race has become too expensive and dangerous.

Fear, suspicion, secrecy, propaganda are at last slowly giving way to the benefits of cooperation and interdependence, despite the opposition of the Sons of Belial.

China, Cradle of Christianity?

In the 1940's, Cayce made some unlikely comments about the future of China. As so often is the case, he was looking from the broad, long-term perspective and not merely at immediate, contemporary events or conditions. At the time, the country was torn with internal strife: civil war between the Communists and the Nationalists; poverty to the point of the people eating dogs and the bark of trees; fighting to fend off the invading Japanese army and air force.

"The sin of China?" Cayce asked. "Yes, there is the quietude that will not be turned aside, saving itself by the slow growth. There has been a growth, a stream through the land in ages which asks to be left alone to be just satisfied with that within itself. It awoke one day and cut its hair off: And it began to think and to do something with its thinking! This, here, will be one day the cradle of Christianity, as applied in the lives of men. Yes, it is far off as man counts time, but only a day in the heart of God—for tomorrow China will awake. Let each and every soul as they come to those understandings, do something, then, in his or her own heart." (*Case #3976-29*; 1944)

China did awake, and the awakening was not so far off; five years later Mao Tse-tung and his revolutionaries drove the corrupt, U.S.-backed Chiang Kai-shek and his war lords out of the country and set up the People's Republic. Atheistic to the core, the new regime's first actions included the suppression of organized religions: Christianity, Taoism, Buddhism, even Confucianism. Far from being the cradle of a new religion of any sort, missionaries were promptly dispatched homeward, accused of being capitalist spies—an accusation that contained a certain amount of truth.

The interests of Mao and Chou-En-Lai were strictly pragmatic, the problems almost overwhelming: How to eliminate the perennial causes of hunger and poverty, pestilence, illiteracy, miserable health care, backward educational and industrial facilities.

But in twenty years the doctrines of Mao—the work ethic, the puritan ethic, the dedicated all-for-one-and-one-for-all ethic—had created the "New Man" in China. She had conquered the heritage of the Sleeping Giant. Essentially a spiritual people, the Chinese had performed a miracle, and the Western world only gradually began to learn of it. Strict Puritans, if there are any saints around today, China has more than her share of them.

Edgar Faure, twice premier of France, described Mao as having "the gestures of a man of religion. He makes me think of the leader of a religious community, of a member of one of the military orders." And that may be the reason child slavery, compulsory marriage, begging, gambling, prostitution, venereal disease, crime, violence, juvenile delinquency have virtually disappeared in the new China. If it has a religion today, it is Mao's little Red Book of ethics, for there is no manifestation of interest in conventional religious institutions.

The Chinese Red Army is probably the world's best disciplined military force. Strict rules were laid down for the troops' behavior during and after the civil war, which must be memorized by every soldier. No confiscation of property belonging to peasants; replace all doors when you leave a house (the wooden doors of Chinese homes were easily detached and often taken down at night, set on blocks and used as beds). Later this became simply, replace any article used. Roll up and return the straw matting on which you sleep. Be courteous and helpful when you can. Return all borrowed articles. Be honest in all transactions with the people. Pay for all articles purchased. Be sanitary, and especially establish latrines at a distance from people's houses. Don't flirt with the women. Don't kill prisoners of war.

Mao is on record as claiming that in all the years of fighting the Japanese, the Red Army never killed a captured soldier. As for internal enemies in a revolutionary period, he once said, "They should not be killed. It is a mistake to believe that by physically eliminating traitors or enemy prisoners, you can serve a revolutionary cause." But many were killed, although he passionately believed in re-education and rehabilitation of the disloyal.

In 1973, the Roman Catholic Church recognized all this and went so far as to make a public overture for a dialogue with Peking, pointing out that "Christian reflections" were present in the thoughts of Chairman Mao. The Vatican's missionary bulletin, *International Fides Correspondence*, hinted that preliminary moves for contacts may already be underway by both sides.

The doctrine inspiring the People's Republic of China, said the bulletin, "contains some directives that are in keeping with the great moral principles of the millenary Chinese civilization, and find authentic and complete expression in modern social Christian teaching." Mao's doctrine is "a moral socialism of thought and conduct . . ." China today "is devoted to a mystique of disinterested work for others, to inspiration by justice, to exaltation of simple and frugal life, to rehabilitation of the rural masses and to a mixing of social classes."

"It was true that Maoist Marxism was atheistic," and the Communist Party "full of prejudices against any religion, and therefore also against Christianity," the Catholic study declared. But some directives of Mao "affirm human values", and the climate had become more favorable for acknowledging the rights of minorities and religious groups, "Christian and others".

The article made clear that the Vatican was anxious to establish communication, and was hopeful that this would soon be possible. Some progress has already been made. In 1971, Catholic churches in Peking and Shanghai were reopened for foreign residents, diplomats and tourists, a tiny chink in the Chinese wall of anti-religion. And some schools are again permitted to teach religion; Nanking has a theological college, Peking, Moslem and Buddhist ones.

Maoism is indeed almost a religion and does reflect many Christian values. He was convinced that human nature is essentially good and its betterment is only a matter of education and environment. But China's becoming "the cradle" for any new Christianity appears remote at present, although it does exhibit some of its values "as applied in the lives of men", as Cayce indicated.

During the civil war a book publisher asked Cayce for advice on "improving the future of cultural relations as they affect books between this country and China in the years after the war." Chiang Kai-shek, a nominal Christian at best and a zealous tyrant at worst, was defeated in 1949.

Answered Cayce: "As will be seen, the greater rule in the next twenty-five years in China is to grow towards the Christian faith . . . though it may appear to some at present that this is lacking . . ." (*Case #2834-3*) If he

had said and meant Christian principles instead of faith,
he could be given a higher mark on this one. Yet in 1938
he did say, referring to the invasion of China by Japan,
that "might does not make right. Rather will the principles of the Christian faith be carried forward in and
through the turmoils that are a part of both China and
Japan." (*Case #3976-19*) Japan has since experienced a
religious upsurge with hundreds of new sects, many
combining Christian and Buddhist elements. Paradoxically, the Chinese are spiritual-minded but have never
been religious.

Would China take a more democratic or more
authoritarian turn, the publisher wanted to know.

"More of the democratic," replied Cayce. "For, as
has been indicated, more and more will those of the
Christian faith come to be in political positions, and this
in China will mean the greater rule in certain groups—
according to how well these manifest. And these will
progress. For, civilization moves west . . . the various
sects in China . . . will all be united, more and more,
towards the democratic way . . . just as it has begun and
as it has been in the last twenty years, and it will grow
and spread faster in the next twenty-five, and more in
the last five than in the first ten." (*Case #2834-3*)

If there is a Christian in political position in China
today, he is discreetly keeping his mouth shut about it.
And there are few "sects". There is nothing to sub-
stantiate what Cayce said on the point. As for the
"democratic" way, Cayce's twenty-five years were up
in 1968, and the country is still largely ruled from the
top down. Mao's state socialism reigns, guided by the
Party Central Committee and the Politburo elected by
some 13,000,000 Party members. At the lower levels,
however, People's Revolutionary Committees make
local decisions. All must work, taking their turn at
manual labor, and women have equal rights with men.
There are no class distinctions. China appears to be as
much a benevolent dictatorship as a people's democracy, for the bureaucracy has veto power over the
locals, and its executives run big industry.

Cayce went so far as to predict that, "If there is not

the acceptance in America of the closer brotherhood of man, the love of the neighbor as self, civilization must wend its way westward . . . and again must Mongolia, must a hated people, be raised." (*Case #3976–15*) That remains to be seen. China and Mongolia are backward countries. Still, the New Man may yet come out of China.

But in another reading he makes unbelievable comments that have no basis in fact with our present knowledge. Referring to the prehistoric Gobi Desert of Mongolia, he said: "As to the manner of locomotions in the experience, the entity injected much of that which . . . when there is the discovery of the Temple of Gold—will be found: lifts or elevators, the one-line electrical car, the very fast aerial locomotion—these were a portion of those experiences with which the entity had much to do . . . The communications—not the telegraph as is known today; more of that of the voice transmission of a quite different type and nature." (*Case #877–11*)

All this in a rocky, barren, windblown desert! With five to eight inches of rainfall, the land supports only the most hardy of creatures—goats, camels, horses, gazelles, and a few Mongolian tribesmen. True, the climate has changed somewhat over the millenia, and prehistoric peoples are known to have lived there, but the land has never been under ice-sheets and therefore subject to radical change. The Sand Dune Dwellers existed 10 to 20,000 years ago, and an older culture dating to 100,000 B.C. But the only artifacts found have been stone implements and pictographs of man and animals. No elevators, street cars, monorails, aircraft. As for a Temple of God, neither the Gobi nor China proper has more than negligible amounts of the metal.

Wars and Rumors of Wars

In 1935, Cayce made some uncanny predictions of a coming holocaust that proved to be all too correct. Hitler had recently come to power in Germany with his politics of hate, but he had not made any military moves against other countries. The world was still in the crunch of depression.

Said Cayce: "As to the affairs of an international nature, these we find are in a condition of great anxiety on the party of many; not only as individuals but as to nations. And the activities that have already begun have assumed such proportions that there is to be the attempt upon the part of groups to penalize, or to make for the associations of groups to carry on same.

"This will make for the taking of sides, as it were, by various groups or countries or governments. This will be indicated by the Austrians, Germans, and later the Japanese joining in their influence; unseen and gradually growing to those affairs where there must become, as it were, almost a direct opposition to that which has been the theme of the Nazi—(the Aryan). For these will gradually make for a growing of animosities.

"And unless there is interference from what may be called by many the *supernatural* forces and influences, that are active in the affairs of nations and peoples, the whole world—as it were—will be set on fire by the militaristic groups and those that are 'for' power and expansion in such associations." (*Case #416-7*)

Three years later Hitler annexed Austria. In 1939, he invaded Poland, and the next year Norway, Denmark, France and the Low Countries. Italy, which Cayce failed to mention, and Japan joined with Germany soon afterwards. The "whole world" was indeed "set on fire by the militaristic groups" he had named.

Yet, on the question of wars and religious differences, he once made a highly dubious remark. "These are the swords He brought into man's material understanding. And more wars, more bloodshed have been shed (*sic*) over the racial and religious differences than over any other problem! These, too, must go the way of all others; and man must learn—if he will know the peace as promised by Him—that God loveth those who love Him, whether they be called of this or that sect or schism or ism or cult! The Lord is ONE!" (*Case #3976-27*)

The poor grammar aside, historians would say that most wars have been fought over economic and territorial issues. Man's greed, ambition and lust for power is greater than his racial and religious prejudice. The drive for land, natural resources, markets motivated most conflicts along with a historic and ambitious sense of achievement in conquering other nations, other peoples. Racial and religious differences played their parts in the distant past—sometimes as a cover for the real purpose—but hardly the major part in the leaderships' desire to dominate, conquer, expand. International wars more often are made by governments, not by peoples.

Cayce made other strange predictions that have little resemblance to fact. In April, 1941, when Europe was aflame with World War II, he said: "Strifes will arise through the period. Watch for them near Davis Strait (between Canada and Greenland) in the attempts there for the keeping of the life line to a land open. Watch for them in Libya and in Egypt, in Ankara and in Syria, through the straits about those areas above Australia, in the Indian Ocean and the Persian Gulf.

"Ye say these are of the sea; yes—for there shall the breaking up be, until there are those in every land that shall say that this or that shows the hand of divine interference, or that it is nature taking a hand, or that it is the natural consequence of good judgments." (*Case #3976-26*)

We have no way of knowing what he expected in these areas; only that "strifes will arise through the period" and a "breaking up". In the context of the reading, the period would be the war, but fighting had already been going on in Libya and Egypt for six months. General MacArthur's Pacific Command did soon go into action "about those areas above Australia", e.g., in the Coral Sea, New Guinea, the Solomon Islands. In Syria, Britain attacked and brought the campaign there to an end. But nothing of note occurred in the Davis Strait, Ankara, the Persian Gulf, or the Indian Ocean. Moreover, nothing recognizable took place suggesting "divine interference" or "nature taking a hand".

In January, 1934, Cayce made what must be the most bizarre prognostication on record. In answer to the question, What are the world changes to come this year physically? he replied: "There will be open waters appear in the northern portions of Greenland. There will be new lands seen off the Caribbean Sea, and dry land will appear. There will be the falling away in India of much of the material suffering that has been brought on a troubled people. There will be the reduction of one risen to power to central Europe to naught. The young king son will soon reign.

"In America in the political forces we see a restabilization of the powers of the peoples in their own hands, a breaking up of the rings, the cliques in many places. South America shall be shaken from the uppermost portion to the end, and in the Artarctic off Tierra del Fuego land, and a strait with rushing waters." (*Case #3976–15*)

None of this happened, of course, and could hardly have happened all in one year. It would have been a calamitous year indeed! And even if Cayce were speaking of a larger period of time—as well he may—he is still on every count wrong to date, after forty years, with the possible exception of Hitler's "reduction" to "naught".

Most incongruous of all is the reign of the "young king son", which a question revealed referred to Germany. Hitler was in power in 1934 and remained so until 1945. The Allied occupation forces ruled until 1949, when Konrad Adenauer was elected chancellor and Theodor Reuss president. In East Germany, Otto Grotewohl and Wilhelm Peick were the top bananas on the stalk. None was a "young king son".

World Affairs Reading

In 1938, Cayce gave a pointed, prophetic dissertation that is worth repeating in its entirety, not only for its significance today but that the reader may make a judgment on a complete reading in context, however right or wrong its claims.

This psychic reading given by Edgar Cayce at his home on Arctic Crescent, Virginia Beach, Virginia, this

24th day of June, 1938, in accordance with request made by Hugh Lynn Cayce, Manager of the Association for Research and Enlightenment, Inc.

PRESENT: Edgar Cayce; Gertrude Cayce, Conductor; Gladys Davis, Stenographer; Hugh Lynn Cayce.

READING: World Affairs—Congress Program
Time of Reading: 10.55 to 11.25 a.m., Eastern Standard.

Mrs. Cayce: You will continue at this time the information given Monday, June 20th, on National and International Affairs, which is to be presented at the Congress (of the Association for Research and Enlightenment) meeting on Monday, June 27th. Please continue this discourse, applying the general principles outlined to present conditions in America and other countries. You will answer the questions that may be asked.

Mr. Cayce: Since the application of those truths or tenets as indicated becomes the basic needs of the peoples of every land in the present, to be sure it behooves those in America, then, to apply same in their dealings with the situations that exist respecting the political, the economic and the general situations throughout the land.

This at the first glance may appear to be an impractical thing; yet these are the conditions to be met: Every phase of human experience and human relationship must be taken into consideration; just as indicated from that given, that we ARE our brother's keeper. Then if those in position to give of their means, their wealth, their education, their position, DO NOT take these things into consideration, there must be that leveling that will come.

For unless these are considered, there must eventually become a revolution in this country—and there will be a dividing of the sections as one against another. For these are the leveling means and manners to which men resort when there is the plenty in SOME areas and a lack of the sustenance in the life of others. These are the manners in which such things as crime, riots and every nature of disturbance arise—in that those who are in authority are not considering every level, every phase of human activity and human experience.

We find these conditions have been in other lands, centralized, localized into individual activities—as in Russia, Italy, Germany; the conditions that exist in Spain, in China, in Japan are what? The oppression of the producers by those for whom and to whom such power has come to be used as their opportunity for becoming their brother's keeper; and not as represented in some lands, the disregarding of the other's right. Then those who are in power must know that they ARE their brother's keeper, and give expression to that which has been indicated in "Thou shalt love the Lord with all thy heart and mind and body, and thy neighbor as thyself."

This rule must be applied. It is true that in some of those factions in Russia this is an attempt, yet there ARE those who have applied and do apply same in not only the economic life but attempt to in the mental and spiritual life. And this brings or works hardships where it should NOT be.

True, in other lands—whether the Communism, the Fascism or the Nazi regime—these are missions to be filled, and these are opportunities. But when there becomes class or mass distinction between this or that group, this or that party, this or that faction, then it becomes a class rather than "thy neighbor as thyself". For all stand as ONE before Him. For the Lord is NOT a respecter of persons, and these things CANNOT long exist.

From the conditions in these other lands, then, America—the United States—must take warning. For to WHOM does the wealth belong? To WHOM do the possibilities of the land belong? Does it belong to those who have inherited it, to those who have been given the positions by power? To those who have by their labor, by the sweat of their brow PRODUCED same?

Not that all would be had in common as in the communistic idea, save as to keep that balance, to keep that oneness, to keep that association of ideas, of activity, of the influences throughout the experiences of all. These are to be kept in those attunements in which there may be the land itself defining what freedom is; in that each soul is by his OWN activity to be given the opportunity of expression, of labor, of production.

But all of these, also, are not to say where or what, but are to seek through their OWN ability, their OWN activity, to give that of themselves that is in keeping with those who labor in the vineyard of the Lord. Hence these may apply in the national and international relationships.

For there must come, first, a stabilization of the monetary unit. There must come then the exchange of commodities or of trade in a way and manner in which not merely sections, not merely distinctions made of one portion of the land against another, but ALL are taken into consideration.

Unless this is done, turmoils and strifes will arise. And that which has made and does make the people of America afraid, is the fear of servitude in ANY manner. All, though, must learn that those who ARE to be the greater, those who would make the greater contributions to activity in every sphere and phase of influence, are to be the servants of all; not those who would be lords over others. For the Lord so loved the world as to give His only begotten Son, that whosoever would might KNOW that life in its manifestations, in its expressions and relationships and dealings as one to another is not a gouging, not a "gimmie", not a hate—not those things that belittle, but those that create hope, faith and understanding in the minds and hearts of men EVERYWHERE!

All that is for the sustenance of life is produced from the soil. Then there must be a return to the soil. Every man must be in that position that he at least creates, by his activities, that which will sustain the body from the soil; or where he is supplying same to those activities that bring such experiences into the lives of all. For of dust the body is made, and of dust the sustenance of same comes. Then the mind and the spirit, in accord with those things indicated, will bring into the experiences of all that relationship one to another wherein that all ARE brethren. For these must bring and keep peace one with another. Ready for questions.

Question: Make such comment as may be presented on the following affairs, as I name them: The unemployment situation in America.

Answer: In all of those centers or areas there must be more and more return to the toil upon the land, and not so much of the makeshift of labor in specific or definite fields. For unless this comes, there must and will come disruption, turmoil and strife.

Question: Labor and capital in America.

Answer: Unless there is the give and the take, and the considerations of those that produce—so that they have as much of the use and the divisions of the excess and profits of the labors—there must be brought turmoils in the land.

Question: The Japanese and Chinese situation.

Answer: These bespeak of themselves that which is happening and has happened. But might does not make right. Rather will the principles of the Christian faith be carried forward in and through the turmoils that are a part of BOTH China and Japan. For without those cleansings and purifyings, tradition alone may *not* be destroyed. For it is through the purging that the strength and the beauty of each will come forth.

Question: The Spanish situation.

Answer: This is that whereunto the real troubles, here, are only beginning. For unless there is to be the consideration given to each factor, then others will come in and devour the spoils. This is the outcome of seed sown in the ages past, and from same man can—as a whole—and SHOULD take warning.

Question: The Russian situation.

Answer: As we have indicated, here a new understanding has and will come to a troubled people. Here, because of the yoke of oppression, because of the self-indulgences, has arisen another extreme. Only when there is freedom of speech, the right to worship according to the dictates of the conscience—until these come about, still turmoils will be within.

Question: The German situation, within its own country and in its relations with others.

Answer: A man that represents a country—So long as there is class and mass distinction, there must be turmoils and strife. But so long as the powers are held within those whose purposes and ideals are that of "I am my brother's keeper", and not forcing self upon same (*sic*). Being the brother's keeper does not mean that I am to tell him what to do, or that he is to do this or that irrespective, but rather that ALL are free before the law and before God.

Question: The Italian situation internally and in relation with others.

Answer: This is being rather an outgrowth; and the dictatorship is becoming more and more in line with those policies of peace—and will BRING peace to many another disturbed quarter and section.

Question: The British situation in its own country and in relation to its colonies.

Answer: This is being balanced, or is the balancing power in the European land as well as in the Far East. And when those activities are set that will bring the consideration of EVERY phase, more and more will it be able to control the world for peace.

In France we find that where an old debt must eventually be paid.

We are through for the present. (*Case #3976-19*)

Conclusion

This study is not intended to be—indeed could not be—an exhaustive, comprehensive survey of the rightness or wrongness of Edgar Cayce. Hopefully, it is representative of his work on some important questions and problems that might be resolved, verified or disputed by our present knowledge, although that itself is not immutable.

As we now know, much of what he had to say is in total or partial disagreement with accepted orthodox science, history, religion. Yet we need to remember there is not just one truth but often several truths. There is no absolute knowledge, and those who claim it only disclose their lack of it. All information is imperfect; communications and the transmission of ideas is hazardous. We only know what we experience, and that is purely subjective. It doesn't *prove* anything to someone else. We therefore live by our own set of beliefs, our perception of "truth". We live by faith. Few ideas are fixed beyond all doubt.

By hindsight, Cayce made some apparent, horrendous mistakes. Yet many of his earliest claims concur with the latest thinking, discoveries, developments by scholars expert in their field. As new breakthroughs are made, he appears to be increasingly accurate. Cayce was *avant-garde*, and that is always perilous. A man who is one step ahead of the crowd is a leader; if two steps ahead he is a radical; if three steps ahead he is mad or a charlatan.

Some of Cayce's dissertations are almost unintelligible. His syntax is the world's worst. Occasionally a reading will sound like so much gobbledygook. Moreover, when he found himself in an untenable and embarrassing position or was asked a vital, key question, he sometimes evaded the issue, preached a sermon, told the inquirer to do something for himself.

His rare show of anger and impatience raises serious questions. Was he really asleep? Were there times when he couldn't put himself "under" but attempted to give the reading anyway? People often came from hundreds of miles away to sit in on their readings. Did Cayce not want to disappoint them? This appears unlikely. Exhausted in his last years, he would sometimes go to sleep and say nothing.

During World War II, a popular magazine ran an article entitled "Miracle Man of Virginia Beach". Cayce was engulfed with a cascade of mail requesting readings on the welfare of sons and husbands overseas. He didn't have the heart to refuse them; he started giving four, six, eight and more readings a day, although the readings themselves had advised only two. By November, 1944, he had received 25,000 requests and was a year behind in appointments and office work. The detail of answering letters and returning proffered money overwhelmed him and his small staff. Apparently a worrier by nature, he suffered from exhaustion and edema of the lungs. During this period, the discourses were often of poor quality, and especially, as always, when the request came from other than the subject himself and without his knowledge.

We have no sure way of knowing the reasons for Cayce's failures. Did his psychic antennae sometimes pick up the wrong wave-length? There were occasions when he seemed to not contact the right subject, e.g., when guided by a newspaper clipping or requests from second—and third—parties not directly involved in the matter. But we do know with some certainty that the character of the man negates any fraudulent activity, and none has ever been uncovered by the most cynical of skeptics.

A frustrated preacher at heart—in his youth he wanted to become a minister but never gained the education—he had a penchant for moralizing. Many of his dissertations are simply sermons, albeit inspiring if repetitious ones. His philosophical generalities make more sense than some of his scientific specifics. He was not averse to bucking the accepted scholarly scheme of things, although he once said, "We're not telling science what to do. We're telling you what to do!"

Cayce's physical health diagnoses and treatments, extensively dealt with in other works, appear to have greater accuracy than, say, his prognostications of future events. Hundreds of readings for specific individuals, couched in correct medical terminology, in provable instances turned out to be valid in that most difficult and convincing of tests—the cure. He correctly gave the temperature and blood pressure of unseen patients, described the location and cause of ailments, named the sex of unborn children. No linguist, he sometimes spoke in foreign languages for persons living in Europe.

Participating and investigating doctors estimate his physical health readings to be between 85 and 90 percent accurate. But the perusal of the discourses here indicates a considerable less degree of correctness—about 72 percent. Based on 37 points of contention in the complete Life Reading, and considering the imponderables of nebulous past-life experiences as being either "likely" or "unlikely", we arrive at a figure of 84 percent accuracy for that reading. This is phenomenal for a person 500 miles away whom Cayce never met and knew nothing of. And it could improve with the passage of time and events, as "Mr. Zee" admits.

In other Life Readings, psychological traits were accounted for in presumed past incarnations, vocational abilities detected and defined—even for newborn infants—and character analyses and environmental circumstances described. Written documents in the files attest to the validity of many of these readings, but not all. They have been explored at some length in other volumes. His "contact" here seems to have been better than on other abstract subject matters. Nevertheless, the Life Readings do not *prove* reincarnation.

Prophecy, of course, is always hazardous. As Cayce remarked, the free will of man is often unpredictable and the course of events is changed. Even God, he once said, does not know what a man will do until he contemplates his choices. This might, but not necessarily, resolve Cayce's failures in predicting earth changes and natural calamities, since he often associated them with the sins of the world.

The first medical man to recognize and work closely with Cayce's diagnostic and curative abilities, Dr. Wesley Ketchum, then of Hopkinsville, Kentucky, observed a vital peculiarity back in 1911. In a paper delivered before the American Association for Clinical Research, he said: "As fixed laws seem to govern all phenomena in nature, it is but natural to infer that this is true of the workings of the psychic.

"In the course of my investigations I have discovered only one thing that seems to be absolute: that is that the patient should in some way solicit help in his or her particular case; otherwise, results are meager. I say this because in several instances where (in) my "Unusual Case" (I) tried to help patients who had no previous knowledge that such was being done for them, he only gave a rambling talk, hitting the subject only in high places, so to speak, or missing it entirely in one case.

"I am here to offer no explanation as to how he works, or the source of his knowledge, because I do not know. I am governed only by results. In all the cases I selected for experiment, he had no knowledge of them, directly or indirectly, until after he was asleep. After he is awakened and is shown a copy of what he has said, he claims to have no knowledge of it in any way, or what the scientific expressions mean."

Therein may lay the key to many of Cayce's failures: the absence of personal solicitation for readings.

Subsequent questions to the sleeping seer revealed the sources of his information, and they may explain why individuals usually received more accurate readings than those on general subject matters.

"Each and every soul entity, or earthly entity, passing through the earth plane radiates in that plane those conditions that are radiated from the soul or spiritual entity of the individual. This, then, becomes the fact, the real fact in the material world. The body—Edgar Cayce—in the psychic or subconscious condition, is able to reach all the subconscious minds when directed to such subconscious minds through suggestion, whether in the material world or in the spiritual world, provided the spiritual entity has not passed entirely into that condition where the radiation or the relative forces are superseded by other radiations. Then we reach only those radiations left in the earth's plane that are taken again when entering the earth's plane, whether the entity is conscious of same or not.

"The consciousness of reaching that condition wherein the physical body may take up that truth known must be reached by all. Hence the given expression, the body, Edgar Cayce, in the subconscious condition may communicate with those passed into the spiritual plane." (*Case #254–24*)

Again he said: "The information as given or obtained from this body (Edgar Cayce) is gathered from the sources from which the suggestion may derive its information. In this state the conscious mind becomes subjugated to the subconscious, superconscious or soul mind, and may and does communicate with like minds, and the subconscious or soul force becomes universal. From any subconscious mind information may be obtained, either from this plane or from the impressions as left by the individuals that have gone before.

"As we see a mirror reflecting direct that which is before it, it is not the object itself but that reflected, as in this: The suggestion that reaches through to the subconscious or soul in this state gathers information from that as reflected from what has been or is called real or material, whether of the material body or of the physical forces. And just as the mirror may be waved or bended to reflect in an obtruse manner, so that suggestion to the soul forces may bend the reflection or that given. Yet within the image itself is what is re-

flected, and not that of some other. Through the forces
of the soul, through the mind of others as presented, or
that have gone before, through the subjugation of the
physical forces, in this manner the body obtains the information . . .

"Just as we know as to the force implied from whatever element the force is given, we must know from that
force the information is obtained—deflected only by the
expression of the individual who obtains the information—by the results obtained in the end . . . In the
spirit force there are good and there are bad personages
still reflected . . . Then judge. Judge, as the seed of truth
is ever the same . . ." (*Case #9415*) Cayce, then, was no
"medium" and had no "guide".

What is one to make of Edgar Cayce and his
"readings"? While for the most part enlightening,
believable, prophetic, they are neither infallible nor
Revelation. His source of information—the unconscious mind of the subject and/or the Akashic Records,
the Collective Unconscious—could conceivably contain
error as well as truth. If his psychic ability was truly
God-given, as he believed—one of the Gifts of the
Spirit—he was perhaps the recipient of some kind of
spiritual guidance. Significantly, some of his most
glaring failures came when seeking material rewards,
such as oil wells and hidden treasures.

Most compelling of all, in forty-three years and
14,246 discourses, his work reveals a lack of internal
contradiction or inconsistency, and not too many patent
errors. That is an extraordinary if not miraculous ac-
complishment. The best and the brightest of us could
not do so well in our conscious, waking state. In dealing
with such enormous, wide-ranging, unwieldy subjects,
one would be overwhelmed.

For an uneducated man asleep hundreds or thousands
of miles away from the subject, Edgar Cayce's successes
go far beyond the reach of chance or coincidence. As
Abraham Lincoln put it, "No man has a good enough
memory to be a successful liar."